A DIRECTORY OF YORK
SILVERSMITHS AND ASSOCIAT

Front Cover: *A gold cup by Marmaduke Best, the gift in 1672 of Marmaduke Rawdon, son of Alderman Laurence Rawdon, to York Corporation.*

Rear Cover: *A pair of silver gilt altar candlesticks by William Mascall, the gift in 1672/3 of Lady Mary Beaumont, eldest daughter of George Burdell of Denby, to York Minster.*

Pear shaped teapot:
Maker John Langwith, 1708
in the Treasury in York Minster Undercroft
(see Foreword)
Photo: Courtesy of the William Lee Collection

A DIRECTORY

OF

YORK

GOLDSMITHS,

SILVERSMITHS

AND

ASSOCIATED CRAFTSMEN

Compiled by

HUGH MURRAY

Sessions Book Trust, York, England

By the same author:

The Horse Tramways of York 1880–1909	1980
Dr Evelyn's York	1983
Servants of Business	1984
Heraldry and the Buildings of York	1985
Photographs and Photographers of York: The Early Years 1844–1879	1986
Outside Micklegate Bar	1988
Nathaniel Whittock's Bird's Eye View of the City of York in the 1850s	1988
Opportunity of Leisure	1989
York through the Eyes of the Artist (with S. Riddick and R. Green)	1990
This Garden of Death	1991
The Yorkshire Architectural and York Archaeological Society: A Sesquicentenary Retrospect 1842–1992	1992
The York Graveyard Guide	1994
The Great Chamber at Gilling Castle	1996
Scarborough, York and Leeds: The Town Plans of John Cossins 1697–1743	1997

First published in 1998
by the Sessions Book Trust

ISBN 1 85072 200 5

Printed by William Sessions Limited
The Ebor Press,
York, England

CONTENTS

v

ILLUSTRATIONS

Frontispiece:
   Teapot: maker John Langwith, 1708.
Following page 160:
   1   Communion cup: maker Robert Harrington, 1622.
   2   Sweetmeat dish: maker James Plumer, 1636.
   3   Wine cup: maker Robert Williamson, 1655.
   4   'Death's Head' spoon: maker Thomas Mangy, 1669.
   5   Fork: maker Thomas Mangy, 1680.
   6   Bleeding bowl: maker John Plumer, 1670.
   7   Wax jack: maker William Busfield, 1695.
   8   Peg tankard: maker John Thompson, 1673.
   9   Chinoiserie porringer: maker Thomas Mangy, 1676.
   10   Tankard: maker Marmaduke Best, 1677.
   11   Coffee pot: maker Hampston, Prince and Cattles, 1799.
   12   Thistle–shaped cup: maker James Barber and William Whitwell, 1821.
   13   Tankard with fox finial: maker Barber, Cattle and North, 1827.
   14   Johnnie Walker Ebor cup: maker Barbara Cattle, 1967.

FOREWORD

It was in 1972 that the well-known Stonegate Antique-dealer, William Lee (1896–1989) published his booklet *York Silver 1475 to 1856* being "a short history of York silver, together with an illustrated catalogue of the William Lee collection". Do not miss the "Tale of a 1708 Teapot" in his Introduction. Then, in 1981, a facsimile second printing was co-published by the Dean and Chapter in association with Sessions of York, and this continues to be available from the latter or from The Minster Bookshop.

Upon William Lee's death in 1989 at the age of 93, this unique collection of York-made silver was donated for permanent display as part of the collection in York Minster's Undercroft Treasury.

Shortly after the original 1972 publication, Mr and Mrs William Lee welcomed my wife and me to their home in order to show us their large and wide-ranging collection of illustrations, newspaper-cuttings and catalogue descriptions on York silver and silversmiths: a truly dedicated accumulation. By that time William Lee, through his professional expertise and lifetime's research, had built up an unrivalled knowledge about all things to do with York Silversmiths and their wares.

Another invaluable source of York silver information, based on original research by Martin Gubbins of London, is his book entitled *The Assay Office and Silversmiths of York: 1776–1858* which was published by Sessions of York in 1983.

It had been intended to build on all this information and produce a comprehensive work on all aspects of York silver but as a preliminary to this Hugh Murray has assembled a directory of the craftsmen concerned taking as his starting point the Freeman's Register, which begins in 1272, but adding information from a large number of primary and secondary sources (see appendix 1). It is not expected that this directory will be exhaustive and the publishers and the author will be grateful to receive additional or amended data which will be made available to future researchers into this visually fascinating and specialist aspect of York's illustrious and varied history.

William K. Sessions   Chairman, Sessions Book Trust

ACKNOWLEDGEMENTS

A study of this magnitude could not have been produced without the help of many persons who have willingly given of their time and expertise. Accordingly I would like to thank Bernard Barr, Sub–librarian, York Minster Library; David Beasley, Librarian, The Goldsmiths' Company, London; Phyllis Benedikz, Librarian, Assay Office, Birmingham; Elizabeth Brewster; Rita Freedman, York City Archivist; Martin Gubbins; Louise Hampston, Archivist, York Minster Library; Amanda Howard, Local Studies Librarian, York Library; Dr Sarah Rees Jones, Centre for Medieval Studies, University of York; Jackie Richardson, Librarian, Assay Office, Sheffield; Philip Stell, Compiler of the Yorkshire Medieval Biographical Data–bank; Richard Sykes; Chris. Webb, Borthwick Institute of Historical Research; Christopher Warner, Harrogate Silver Dealer; Ivison and Louise Wheatley, Clerk and Assistant Archivist to the Company of Merchant Adventurers of York; York Women's and Craftsmens' Wills Group at the Centre for Medieval Studies, University of York. A special word of thanks is due to Peter and Ann Rycraft who translated the 1411 York Goldsmiths' Ordinances from the original French text.

Hugh Murray

INTRODUCTION

The working of precious metals for coins, ornaments and utilitarian vessels and other objects has been carried out in York for many centuries. Royal and Archiepiscopal mints had been established in the city as early as the eighth century and many moneyers were employed in them. For example, the kings Eandred (807–41) and Ethelred II (841–50) had thirty–two and thirty–four respectively, their names recorded on the coins they produced.[1] Craftsmen producing ornaments and domestic articles, on the other hand, must have been working in the city at the same time but little or nothing is known of them.

The earliest York reference found to a member of the goldsmith's craft is in a document from the second half of the twelfth century in which Robert, *aurifaber*, is mentioned.[2] From that time to the present day well over 500 persons have been described as goldsmiths, either in Latin, French or English, while many more worked with precious metals. This latter category includes goldbeaters, goldfiners, silversmiths, jewellers and watchmakers as well as apprentices for whom there is no record of their trading in their own right or working as a journeyman.

While the goldsmiths of York were once organised in a craft gild no records of their company have survived apart from occasional references in the Corporation records. The directory has therefore been compiled from a large number of other sources including the charters of such organisations as the Merchant Adventurers and the Vicars Choral of York Minster, the Registers of Freemen and Apprentices, Parish Registers, Wills in the York Registry, Lay Subsidy Rolls, Street Directories and Newspapers.

A chronological list composed of what purports to be entirely York goldsmiths flourishing between 1313 and 1851 was compiled by Robert Charles Hope (1855–1926), an antiquarian who lived in Scarborough between 1875 and 1900. It was published by Sir Charles Jackson in *English Goldsmiths and their Marks*. Jackson's treatment of the Chester goldsmiths was thought to be 'most inadequate' by Charles Oman[3]. The same criticism may be levelled at the York list which, on close examination, was found to be not exclusively confined to goldsmiths and, indeed, to contain a number of errors including some incorrect transcriptions of manuscript records. While this list was useful as a starting point every effort has been made to find the original record from which it was compiled. In the course of this search many new records were found which made it possible to add to

1

the list, particularly prior to 1313, and to extend the known dates during which each individual craftsman lived or flourished.

Hope has also uncritically accepted the Freedom dates from the 'Registers of the Freemen of York' edited by Dr Francis Collins for publication by the Surtees Society (Volumes 94 and 102 published in 1897 and 1900 respectively). Collins made no attempt to reconcile the various dating systems used in the registers. The Freemen are listed under the regnal year in which the chamberlains and mayor were elected, a date changed in 1375 from the feast of St Michael (29 September) to the feast of the Purification of the Virgin Mary (2 February) and then in 1483 to the feast of St Blaise (3 February). The regnal and mayoral years did not commence or finish on the same day and, in any case, did not coincide with calendar years, themselves somewhat enigmatic until 1752 when New Year's Day was moved from 25 March [Old Style] to 1 January [New Style]. With all these difficulties the division of the lists into neat calendar years was clearly impossible. In general Collins's dates relate to the Old Style year in which the mayor took office and should, after 1375, be, more correctly, increased by 1.[4]

The inclusion of the clock and watchmakers in the directory may be thought somewhat anomalous but their association with the goldsmiths had occurred as early as the 14th century. John Lovell, free as a goldsmith in 1376 was trading, five years later, as an 'orlogemaker' in the parish of St Mary, Castlegate.[5] When in 1614, due to a lack of a these craftsmen in the city, William Kidson was offered his freedom gratis he was described as 'very skilful in making silver clocks and watches'.[6] This affinity was recognised in Chester when in 1664 the two crafts joined together to form the Company of Goldsmiths and Watchmakers[7] and in Newcastle where some watchmakers registered their marks with or had their silver assayed by the Goldsmiths' Company there.[8] These associations may form the precedent which led to their inclusion in the list compiled by Hope. Certainly silver and gold was used in the products emanating from their workshops.

Clockmakers used silver spandrels to decorate the faces of bracket and long case clocks while watchmakers fitted their mechanisms into cases made both of silver and gold. These accoutrements may, of course, have been bought in, manufactured by the appropriate craftsmen. On the other hand, when a gold box was required to house the York Freedom scroll to be presented to the Prince of Wales in 1789 it was William Clark, a clock and watchmaker of Low Ousegate, who had been apprenticed to the clockmaker, Henry Hindley, who was chosen to make it, perhaps on the strength of the successful completion of a commission he was given in 1780 to repair some of the silver plate in the Mansion House.[9]

The straying of one craft into the speciality of another was not confined to watchmakers. That goldsmiths used their skills to work with other metals is known from an entry in the accounts rolls of Bishop Richard Barnes of Durham (1575–1587). In 1582 the sum of 32s was paid to 'the gouldesmythe at Yorke for a plate to sett over Mrs Barnes'. This plate, a brass, was in the church of St Andrew, Auckland and commemorated Fridesmonda (Giffard) Barnes who died in 1581. It is unfortunate that the goldsmith concerned was not named.[10]

The inclusion of other associated crafts in the directory is less controversial and their relevance is more obvious. Gold–beaters, makers of gold leaf, appear in York documents from 1184 until at least 1403. Strangely the first reference to the craft quoted in the *Oxford English Dictionary* is in 1415 when it appears in the introduction to the York Mystery Plays. In the *Ordo Paginarum* they are linked with the goldsmiths and money–makers.[11] Goldfiners, refiners of gold, make a brief appearance between 1534 and 1574 while silversmiths separated from goldsmiths, who traditionally worked with both metals, in 1721 and continue their distinction to the present day. In an Act of 1300[12] goldsmiths were required not to set any stone in gold unless it was natural, an implication, that jewels were the province of that craft. John Wyclif, in his translation of the Old Testament made in 1382, refers in Jeremiah xxiv,1 to 'Jeconye the son of Joachym ... and the smyth and his iueler' but in 1388 the jeweller became a goldsmith. In York jewellers make a fleeting appearance in the Register of the Freemen between 1413 and 1486 and then disappear until 1690 after which they are conspicuous as a craft in their own right.

That the directory should start with the earliest known records of the craftsmen concerned is without question but the finishing date is more problematic. While the effective closing of the York Assay office in 1858 marked the end of local hallmarking it did not necessarily mean the end of local manufacture or, at least, repair. Tradesmen can still be found after this date described as 'working' but many, in an era at the advent of mass production in large establishments elsewhere, must have bought in the products sold in their shops. Some, however, few in number, sent their wares to other Assay Offices for hallmarking. Thus 1900 has been chosen as the general terminal date for the directory but a few known manufacturing silversmiths after that date have been included.

While the Register of Freemen is an important source for all craftsmen and tradesmen working in York they only cover the area over which the mayor and his council had jurisdiction. In medieval times the city was under the jurisdiction of several different authorities. Independent from the Corporation were the liberty of St Peter controlled by the Dean and Chapter of York Minster, the liberty of St Mary which covered both the precinct of the abbey and the contiguous hamlet of Marygate, the liberty of St Leonard's hospital, the liberty of the King's Forester at Davy Hall in Davygate and, finally, York Castle where royal authority prevailed. The situation was further complicated by a charter of Richard II in 1383 which granted and confirmed that 'the lord mayor &c. should not enter within the Minster yard [the cathedral close] or Bedern, or any houses of canons &c. within or *without* to exercise any jurisdiction. In the latter category Francis Drake lists 140 individual houses in the city and suburbs, as well as an unspecified number included as complete sides of streets. Much of Petergate (17 houses on the south side between Bootham Bar and the Old Deanery, all the houses on the south side between Minstergates and Grape Lane, and all the houses on the north side), Stonegate (14 houses) and Goodramgate (33 houses) were outside municipal jurisdiction.[13] Any craftsmen occupying properties belonging to the canons of York Minster did not necessarily have to become freemen of York to practise their occupation in the city. Their existence is thus only known from other records. The privileges of freemen were extinguished by the Municipal Corporations Act (1836) by which time the effective boundary of the liberty of St Peter within the city had shrunk to Minster Yard and the Bedern, a jurisdiction largely abolished by the expiration in 1838 of the commission of peace granted to the Dean and Chapter by William IV and their decision not to apply for its continuance. The City of York Improvement Act of 1825 had required the householders of this area to elect four commissioners to be responsible for the lighting, paving, cleansing and policing the streets within the liberty. With the supersession of the 1825 Act in 1850 the city's control over the liberty was complete.[14]

THE YORK GOLDSMITHS COMPANY

During the fourteenth century, possibly because of legislation in 1363[15], the craftsmen in York had begun to organise themselves into self–regulating gilds, akin to trade unions, which gave them, subject only to supervision from the corporation, the means to protect their common interests and ensure that agreed standards of workmanship were maintained. The statute concerned required the crafts to appoint two searchers whose intended role was to prevent the making of secret agreements and the employment of monopolistic trading practices. The reverse was, in fact, the case as the searchers, rather than regulating their crafts, became the representatives of their interests and a focus for the formation of gilds.[16] By the end of the fourteenth century more than forty such gilds had come into existence in York, all organised on similar lines under the control of wardens with searchers appointed from amongst their number to check that no faulty work was produced by their fellows.[17] It is not known when the Goldsmiths' gild was formed but as three searchers were elected on 27 August 1404 it is clear that their gild was already in existence then.[18] This is confirmed by the *Ordo Paginarum* of 1415 which allocates, appropriately, responsibility for performing in the Corpus Christi pageant *The Coming of the Three Kings from the East* to the 'Goldsmythes, Orfeuers, Goldbeters and Monemakers'.[19]

As early as 1247 a goldsmith in York had been selected to supervise the quality of coinage produced by the local mint. The chief municipal officers had been commanded by writ, to choose, by the oaths of 12 good men, three trusty persons, one to be moneyer, another for the assay and a third as *Custos Cuneorum*.[20] This requirement was soon changed. At the trial of the pix held at Westminster on 2 March 1247/8 the list of the officials appointed to each of the provincial mints includes the names of four moneyers, four keepers, two assayers and a clerk,[21] a position confirmed in 1249 when Henry III sent a mandate to sixteen towns, including York, requiring that 'in Full Town–Court they should chuse by oath of four and twenty Goodmen Four persons of the most Trusty and Prudent of their Town for the Office of Moneyours in That Town and other Four Like persons for the keeping of the kings Mint There and Two Fit and Prudent Goldsmiths to be Assayours of the money to be made There and one Fit and Trusty Clerk for the keeping of the Exchange'.[22]

While these measures were aimed at regulating the coinage they did nothing to ensure that ornaments and vessels were similarly treated. This had to wait until 1300 when a statue was enacted which ordained that 'no Goldsmith of England, nor none otherwise within the King's Dominion, shall from henceforth make, any Manner of Vessel, Jewel, or any Thing of gold or Silver, except it be of good and true Allay, that is to say, Gold of a certain Touch, and Silver of the Sterling Allay,

5

or of better, at the Pleasure of him to whom the Work belongeth: and that none work worse Silver than Money'. The act recognised that some Goldsmiths' Gilds were already in existence by requiring the wardens of the craft to assay all silver and mark it with the Leopard's Head, as a guarantee of its quality, before it was allowed to leave the manufacturer. Similarly gold had to be no worse than the 'Touch of Paris' and the wardens had to go from 'Shop to Shop among the Goldsmiths' to ensure their gold met the defined standard. To set national standards the statute directed that 'all the good Towns of England where any Goldsmiths be dwelling shall make the same Statutes as they of London be'. One representative of the goldsmiths in every town had to go to London 'for to be ascertained of their Touch' i.e. to ensure that all goldsmiths through out the country were working to the same standard. The penalty for infringing these regulations was 'by Imprisonment or by Ransom at the King's Pleasure'.[23] This requirement for provincial goldsmiths to go to the capital was included in the charter granted in 1327 which gave legal recognition to the control of the craft as a whole by the London company. To ensure that their ordinances were faithfully observed in the north the London company appointed two York goldsmiths for this task, with the authority of the king's writ, in 1330.[24]

The implication of the 1300 Act was that the goldsmiths in York, and elsewhere, should be regulated by ordinances similar to those of London with wardens to ensure compliance to them. In other words the goldsmiths were required to form themselves into a craft gild and this may have already happened when the 1363 statute was enacted as, unlike most other crafts, the standards for the materials with which goldsmiths worked were laid down by statute. Certainly it was in existence by 1404 when three searchers were elected, rather than two, the practice in other gilds. This situation caused a dispute which necessitated a ruling by the mayor on 5 March 1410/11. His decision was that two searchers and no more, both to be Englishmen born, should be chosen and sworn. The mayor, his fellow aldermen and other wise men of the Council Chamber also required that the goldsmiths were to bring their touches for inspection and those who had no mark were to make suitable punches as the law demanded. If any article of gold or silver was sold not marked with the common touch of the city and the mark of the goldsmith who made it, he was liable to a fine of 6s 8d. Other ordinances were made at this time regulating the training of apprentices.[25]

Twelve years after this ruling by the mayor of York a statute was enacted to define 'The Fineness of Harness of Silver and the marks with which it shall be marked'. This act ordained that 'in the City of York, Newcastle upon Tine, Lincoln, Norwich, Bristow, Salisbury, and Coventry, that every one shall have divers Touches, according to the Ordinance of the Mayors, Bailiffs, or Governors of the same Towns.' Additionally the goldsmiths were to have marks, known to the wardens of the craft, to distinguish the articles which they had made. No goldsmith, other worker in silver or the keeper of the civic touch was to put on sale or even mark any silver unless it was as fine in allay as sterling silver except for any solder which was necessary in the manufacture on pain of forfeiture of double the value of the article.[26]

On 10 April 1561 'the auncient ordynancs of the mystery or occupacon of goldsmythes of the Citie of York' were diligently perused, examined and duly reformed by the corporation. This may have been done in the knowledge that the London company were about to make searches in the north under the terms of its 1327 charter, which had been reconfirmed with additions in 1462. This gave it strengthened control over the craft in fairs, markets and towns throughout England and all local officials and mayors were required to assist them. For the time being, however, the north was to escape this control as the London company confined the exercise of its powers to the south until the 16th century.[27] Whatever the reason, the York company's ordinances were revised in time for the searches made in the city by the London goldsmiths on 5 February 1561/2.[28]

The earlier ordinances of 1411 were confirmed and additions were made to bring them into line with various statutes which had been enacted in the intervening years. Significantly in these revisions the common touch or pounce [punch] of the city was defined for the first time as 'the halfe lepard head and half flowre de luyce', in other words a leopard's head and a fleur–de–lis dimidiated and conjoined.[29] From about this time, although not defined in these ordinances, York silver was marked with a date mark in addition to the city and makers' marks, the initials letters of their forenames and surnames. The earliest known date mark is the letter B, on a seal top spoon made by Robert Bekwith. From later letters of known date it can be deduced that the series started at the beginning of the reign of Elizabeth I who came to the throne on 17 November 1558.[30] Jackson claims that the leopard's head and fleur–de–lys may have been replaced in 1632 by a new mark, a fleur–de–lys and rose dimidiated and conjoined,[31] but this is more probably due to a misreading of an impression produced by a worn or recut punch.

7

In spite of this review and subsequent revision of long standing ordinances not all eventualities were covered. The masters and brethren of the goldsmiths asked the lord mayor on 3 February 1585/6 to revise the Ordinal as it did not appear 'howe and in what order' the searchers should be chosen and how their accounts should be audited and presented. After their deliberate perusal of the Ordinal the lord mayor and his court decided that for 'the better quietness of the said occupacon and the benefit of this Cittie' that the old searchers should call together at St Anthony's Hall on the fourth day after the feast of St James the Apostle (25 July) their brethren to elect new searchers for the next year, the old searchers having no vote. After the election and before the masters dispersed the old searchers were to deliver their accounts to the new searchers, their necessary expenses for the previous year to be approved by another vote.[32] Nine years later, in 1596, as a result of goldsmith John Share buying 'moulten silver of a person unknowne which is suspected not to be trewlie or wellcome to by the seller', the mayor required the goldsmiths to bring their Ordinary to his next court so that it could be examined to see if there was an article forbidding such transaction and, if not, one should be added.[33]

Another ten years were to elapse before the next problem arose that required an adjudication from the lord mayor and his court, this time at the behest of the municipal authorities who were concerned that the company of goldsmiths had grown too large and was liable to increase further in size. The rationale behind this concern is not readily apparent. The number of goldsmiths in the city had risen gradually from the seven in the second half of the thirteenth century to 84 in the similar period 300 years later and 87 for the following period. Then for the next five 50 year periods there were never more than 57 and never less than 47, the figure for the period leading up to 1600. In fact after the new measures to limit recruitment were introduced in 1606 the number of goldsmiths rose to 57 during the next 50 years.

At its meeting on 23 July 1606 the Council agreed that, unless he had served as an apprentice within the city with a free brother of the goldsmiths company, no goldsmith should be admitted as a freeman of the city without the consent of the lord mayor and Aldermen provided that the searchers had not been able to object to the sufficiency of the applicant. No free citizen or other inhabitant of York and its suburbs or of any Liberty or privileged place in or near York was to commission any goldsmith who was not a freeman of York and a member of the goldsmiths' company to make alter or exchange any manner of plate or anything else properly part of the work of a goldsmith. Neither was any member of the goldsmiths' company allowed to place work with another goldsmith who was not both a freeman and a company member. The penalty for infringing these requirements was a fine of 40s.

A fourth provision made at this time was that a goldsmith living in the City, the suburbs or Minstergarth [The Liberty of St Peter] who was not a member of the goldsmiths' company should not have the benefit of having his work 'pounced with the towche and marke belonging to this cittye called the half Leopard head and half flowere de Luce' without the consent of the lord mayor.[34] The latter two ordinances were an attempt by the municipal authorities to bring under their jurisdiction the goldsmiths who lived and worked in any of the liberties which were otherwise outside civic control. Only in the case of the goldsmiths, whose work had to be officially marked, was there a sanction which could be imposed with the full authority of the law of the land. This was much more effective than an earlier attempt to bring the liberties under civic control. The MPs for York in 1584 had been instructed to seek but failed to gain legal authority for the searchers of all occupations in the city to be allowed to search such artificers that lived in the close of York.[35]

By the end of the seventeenth century the goldsmiths' company was losing its influence over the control of the practice of the craft in the city. On 1 September 1684 the council found, as a result of a complaint from Barbara Owram, that the company had failed to appoint any searchers. She was awarded relief of 3d a week to be paid by the company who were themselves fined 40s a man for failing to meet the requirements of their Ordinary. They were instructed to meet 'this day fortnight' to chose new searchers.[36] Eleven years later the company's control of the craft appeared to be over. In 1695 the goldsmiths' company were required to hand over its Ordinary into the keeping of the lord mayor until further order,[37] perhaps a precursor of an Act passed in 1696 'to encourage the bringing in of wrought Plate to be coined'.[38]

As the goldsmiths and other workers in silver were not obliged to make plate of any finer silver than Sterling (92.5% silver) the result was that 'Persons regarding their own private gain more than the Publick good' had taken to the craftsmen silver coins of the realm to be converted into vessels and plate. A new minimum standard required all plate to be not less in fineness than 11 ounces and 10 pennyweight of fine silver in every pound Troy (95.84% silver). It was to be marked with 'the Worker's Mark, to be expressed by the two first Letters of his

Surname, the Marks of the Mystery or Craft of the Goldsmiths, which instead of the Leopard's Head and the Lion shall for this plate be the Figure of a Lion's Head erased and the Figure of a Woman, commonly called Britannia' together with a variable mark for the year of manufacture. This standard of silver was known as New Sterling or the Britannia Standard.

The ill–conceived wording of this Act had the effect of closing the old provincial Assay offices but the triumph of the London Company of Goldsmiths was to be short lived.[39] The remoteness of London from other parts of the Kingdom placed the goldsmiths in provincial towns under 'Great difficulties and Hardships in the Exercise of their Trades for want of Assayers in convenient places to assay and touch their Wrought Plate'. Thus in 1700 York, Exeter, Bristol, Chester and Norwich (Newcastle was included by a later Act in 1702[40]) 'the Goldsmiths, Silversmiths, and Plateworkers, who are or shall be Freemen of, or inhabiting within,... and having served an Apprenticeship to the said Trade of goldsmith, Silversmith, or Plateworker, shall be ... incorporated into a Company of or belonging to such city shall be called and known by the Name of the company of Goldsmiths of such City'. Two wardens, to be elected annually, were to be appointed together with 'an able and skilful man to make the assays and to touch the silver with five marks, the Lion's Head erased, Britannia, the arms of the City, a year letter in Roman characters, and the maker's mark, the first two letters of his surname. instead of the initials letters of his forename and surname.[41] By this Act the York Company of Goldsmiths was re–established, the city's arms *[argent] on a cross [gules] five lions passant gardant [or]* replacing the earlier punch.

By 1716 it appears that no individual could be found to take on the duties of assayer at York even though the Act of 1700 allowed him to take eight grains from every pound Troy of silver assayed, four grains to be put into the Box of Diet and the other four grains to be allowed towards his 'Waste and Spillings in making the said Assays'. The result was that two York goldsmiths, John Langwith and Joseph Buckle, took their plate to Newcastle for assay, a round trip of 176 miles, with all the perils to be experienced on the roads at that time. The Minutes of the Goldsmiths' Company of Newcastle record their annual payments of £1 each for assaying paid in arrears. Buckle paid his dues from 1717 to 1719 and Langwith from 1717 to 1721; both failed to make any payment in 1722 although called upon to do so.[42]

From a parliamentary enquiry in 1773 it is known that the York

Assay office was still closed at that time but within a few years it had been revived when, in accordance with statutes enacted in the intervening years, the old sterling standard was restored[43] and the maker's mark reverted to earlier practice of the initials of his forename and surname.[44] The lion's head erased and Britannia were replaced with a crowned leopard's head and a lion passant, and, after 1 December 1784 when plate duty was re–imposed, the monarch's head was added.[45] From the new series of date letters initiated at this time it has been postulated that the year of re–opening was 1776 although no earlier letter than D for 1779 has been discovered.[46] This was probably due to the formation of the business of Hampston and Prince in 1770[47] whose expansion would be aided considerably by presence of a local assay office. This firm existed under a variety of names as partners came and went until 1859 when James Silburn Barber sold it to Heselgrave and Walker, former employees of his father, James Barber, who had died in 1857.[48] For all the nineteenth century life of this firm the assay masters of the York mint were either employees of the firm or had a direct family connection with it.

For three decades at the beginning of the nineteenth century the assay master was William Graves North, a whitesmith and father of a partner in one of the principal businesses in precious metals in York. Articles for assay had to be taken to his Feasegate premises by nine o'clock on Tuesday and Friday mornings and would be ready for collection, after assay and marking, at five o'clock on the same day. If articles were found to be below the legal standard after three separate assays they were destroyed. The assay master's charges were not allowed to exceed sixpence [2.5p] for every pound, troy weight, of silver assayed but he was permitted to take eight grains from each pound of silver, weighed in its unfinished state. These procedures would, it was hoped, prevent 'a system of gross fraud, which would otherwise be practised upon the public, and injure both society in general, and the honest tradesman in particular'.[49]

In 1849 the London manufacturers complained about the mismanagement of the provincial offices 'which through error or design, the public are defrauded' preventing them carrying on business on equal terms. The Board of Inland Revenue in 1851 directed that inspections should be made of the six provincial offices. The committee of inspection, the inspector–general of stamps and taxes and the wardens from the London Goldsmiths Company, found, at York, that no assays had been carried out for some time, the apparatus for making the assays was deposited in a lumber closet and covered with

11

rust and dirt, and the assay master was a worn–out spoon maker, in the employ of Mr Barber, quite unfit for his duties. It was not until 1854 that the report, along with those for the other offices, was brought to the attention of the Treasury and a parliamentary bill was prepared the next year for the abolition of the offices at York, Exeter, Chester and Newcastle–upon–Tyne. The bill was eventually withdrawn and a select committee appointed to inquire into the assaying offices. Despite recommending the consolidation of the many statutes governing the conduct of the offices into one, which would also lay down the procedures for setting them up and closing them down, nothing was done. It was probably the death of James Barber, prime warden of the York Goldsmiths Company, in 1857 which brought about the retirement of the worn–out spoon maker, the end of the Company and, in c.1858, the effective closure of the York assay office. Another assay master appears to have been appointed but he can have had no duties to perform.[50] The sole surviving record of the revived assay office at York is one ledger covering the period 1805–1821, now in York Minster Library.[51]

After 1858 working silversmiths in York had to go elsewhere to have their work assayed. The Newcastle office, for similar reasons, had closed a few years later and the alternatives were Sheffield (opened 1773) Birmingham (opened 1773) and London. That only a handful of commercial silversmiths in York registered marks at these offices is an indication that the manufacturing of articles in precious metals, carried on in the city for over 700 years, had virtually died out and the tradesmen describing themselves as 'working' were engaged only in repair work.

NOTES

1. R. Davies *Historical Notices of the Royal and Archiepiscopal Mints and Coinages of York* (1854);
   G. Benson 'Coins: especially those relating to York' *Yorkshire Philosophical Society Annual Report* (1914).
2. Rees Jones, S. *Medieval Title Deeds for the City of York 1080–1530* (computer work plus documentation) Colchester: ESRC Data Archive (1996) charter 1885.
3. M.H. Ridgway *Chester Goldsmiths from early times to 1726* (1968) p. vii.
4. F. Collins (ed.) 'Register of the Freemen of the City of York, Vol 1, 1272–1558' *Surtees Society 96* (1897) p. xii;

D.M. Palliser 'The York Freemen's Register 1273–1540: Amendments and Additions' *York Historian 12* (1995) p. 21.

5. Collins, F. 'Register of the Freemen of the City of York, Vol 1, 1272–1558' *Surtees Society* 96 (1897) p. 73;
    N. Bartlett 'Lay Poll Tax Returns for the City of York in 1381' *Transactions of the East Riding Antiquarian Society* 30 (1953)

6. York City Archives (YCA) B34 f. 48b.

7. M.H. Ridgway *Chester Goldsmiths from early times to 1726* (1968) p. 86.

8. M.A.V. Gill *A Directory of Newcastle Goldsmiths* 1980

9. York City Archives (YCA) B44 20 July 1789; Chamberlains Accounts C43 30 August 1789; B44 25 February 1780.

10. J. Raine A Brief Historical Account of the Episcopal Castle or Palace at Auckland (1852) p. 72;
    C.H. Hunter Blair 'Durham Monuments' *The Publications of the Newcastle upon Tyne Records Committee* 5 (1925) p. 179.

11. A.F. Johnston & M. Rogerson *Records of Early English Drama: York* (1979) p. 19.

12. 28 Edward I Stat. 3 Cap 20 (1300).

13. F. Drake *Eboracum* (1736) pp. 550 and 552;
    J.S. Purvis A Medieval Act Book (n.d.) pp. 41–45.

14. A Leak 'The Liberty of St Peter of York 1800–1838' *Borthwick Paper* 77 (1990) pp. 2, 22 and 27.

15. 37 Edward III cap 6.

16. S. Rees Jones 'York's Civic Administration 1354–1464' *York 600: The Government of Medieval* (1997) York University of York, Borthwick Studies in History 3.

17. M. Sellers (ed.) 'York Memorandum Book A/Y Part 1 (1776–1419)' *Surtees Society 120* (1912) p. xxiv;
    J.E. Coleclough 'The Craft Gilds of York' *The Craft Gilds* (1952) p. 18.

18. M Sellers (ed.) *op. cit.* in note 16 p. 248.

19. A.F. Johnston and M. Rogerson *Records of Early English Drama: York* 1 (1978) p. 19.

20. R. Davies *op. cit.* in note 1 p. 29: Pat. 32 Hen III m4.

21. Sir Henry Ellis *Chronica Johannes de Oxenedes* (1859) pp. 315–325: Ms Hargrave Brit. Mus. Cod. membrane 313 f. 95b.

22. T. Madox *The History and Antiquities of the Exchequer* (1711) p. 604: Memor 33 Henry III Rot 1a.

23. 28 Edward I Stat. 3 C. 20 (1300).
24. T.F. Reddaway *The Early History of the Goldsmiths' Company 1327–1509* (1975) p. 4.
25. M Sellers (ed.) *op. cit.* in note 16 pp. 74–77 & 248.
26. 2 Henry VI Cap. 14 (1423).
27. T.F. Reddaway *op. cit.* in note 24 pp. 139 & 207.
28. London Goldsmiths Company Minute Book K p. 176.
29. YCA House Book B33 ff. 11b–13.
30. C.J. Jackson *English Goldsmiths and their Marks* (1949) pp. 280 & 285;
    W.J. Cripps *Old English Plate* (1876) pp. 403/4.
31. C.J. Jackson *op. cit.* in note 26, p.281.
32. YCA B28 ff. 185/185b 3 February 1585.
33. YCA B31 f. 228 4 November 1596.
34. YCA B33 fos 23b/24.
35. YCA B28 fo. 164b 14 November 1584.
36. YCA B38 fo. 210 1 September 1684.
37. YCA B39 fo. 26b 18 August 1695.
38. 8 William III Cap. 8 (1696).
39. M.A.V. Gill 'The Latter Days of the York Assay Office' *Yorkshire Archaeological Journal* 49 (1977) p. 115.
40. 1 Anne Cap. IX (1702).
41. 12 & 13 William III Cap. 4 (1700).
42. M.A.V. Gill *op. cit.* in note 35, p. 115;
    M.A.V. Gill *A Directory of Newcastle Goldsmiths* (1980) pp. 68 and 152.
43. 6 George I Cap 11 (1720).
44. 12 George II Cap. 26 (1739).
45. M. Gubbins *York Assay Office and Silversmiths 1776–1858* (1983) p. 34
46. C.J. Jackson *op. cit.* in note 36 p. 292;
    M. Gubbins *op. cit.* in note 41 pp. ix and 70.
47. *York Courant* 20 November 1770.
48. *Yorkshire Gazette* 11 April 1857, 24 July 1858, 12 March, 2 July 1859.
49. W. Hargrove *History and Description of the Ancient City of York* 2 (1818) p. 660.
50. M. Gubbins *op. cit.* in note 41, pp. 1–8, 45–54.
51. York Minster Library Ms Add. 134.

DIRECTORY

(References – see Appendix 1, * Maker's Mark – see Appendix 2)
In general surnames are recorded as they appear in the Register of Freemen, with alternatives found elsewhere included in brackets at the end of the heading to each entry. Forenames have been rendered, where possible, into their modern form. Dates before 1 January 1752 are shown in 'Old Style' when the new year's day was 25 March. Thus 24 March 1750 was followed by 25 March 1751.

Abell

Goldsmith, Free 1272 (SS96/1)

Acey, Peter (Acy, Asee, Asey)

Clockmaker of York, 1638–56 (Dinsdale/41)
Married Joan Leckenby 28 May 1634 Holy Trinity, Goodramgate (PReg)
Buried 19 January 1638 Holy Trinity, Goodramgate (PReg)
Father of Jonathan Acey (baptised 9 July 1635 Holy Trinity, Goodramgate), cordwainer, Free by patrimony 1656 (SS102/119)

Adam

The goldsmith
Tenant of land in Petergate 1220x1228 (YASRS148/286)

Addinell, George

Son of Robert Addinell, Innkeeper of Selby, apprenticed to William Astley (q.v.), indenture 9 February 1808, 7 years, consideration 18 gns (YCA D15/215)
Goldsmith of Gowthorpe, Selby, assays at the York Office, 1817–20 (YAJ49/118)

Addison, John

Son of Elizabeth Addison, widow of Askrigg, aged 14, apprenticed to Joseph Hindley (q.v.), clock and watch maker, 29 August 1769, 7 years, consideration £50 (YCA D14/116) tax of £1 5s paid 29 August 1769 (PRO)
Clock and watch maker of Bridlington, Free 1789 (Malden)

Agar, Charles

Son of John Agar the younger, clock and watch maker, apprenticed to his father, indenture 4 July 1770, 7 years, consideration faithful service (YCA D14/123)
Free 1779 (Malden)
Clock and watchmaker of Selby, married Mary daughter of Thomas Ellison, innkeeper of Barkston Ash 2 February 1783 St Michael, Spurriergate (PReg)
Watchmaker of Pontefract 1784 (Poll)
Buried 27 Dec 1791 Selby (HM)

Agar, Francis

Born 18 April 1787 Selby, son of Charles Agar (q.v.) (HM)
Watchmaker of Pavement, succeeded his uncle, Thomas Agar (q.v.) (YkCo 4 May 1807)
Clock and watchmaker, Free pp 24 November 1808 (Malden)

15

Married Mary daughter of William Atkinson of Leppington 12 January 1809 Scrayningham (HM)

Agar, John

Watchmaker, Free by order 1760 (Malden)

Married Mary Atkinson 2 December 1750 St Olaves (PReg)

Watchmaker of Castlegate 1784 (Poll)

Son, Thomas Agar (q.v.), taken into partnership (YH 12 November 1791)

Of Castlegate, died 21 March, buried St Olaves 24 March 1815 aged 85 (YkCo 27 March 1815, PReg)

Agar, John (junior)

Apprenticed to his father, John Agar, watchmaker (q.v.), indenture 10 September 1766, 7 years (YCA D14/91)

Married Hannah daughter of John Monkman 21 December 1780 Wharram Percy (HM)

Watchmaker, Free 1782 (Malden)

Watchmaker of Malton 1784 (Poll)

Watchmaker of Malton, buried 13 November 1814, St Leonard's, New Malton (HM)

Agar, John

Watchmaker

Son of John Agar (Free 1782), baptised 23 February 1782 St Michael, New Malton (HM)

Watchmaker, Free by patrimony 9 June 1807 (Malden)

Watchmaker of Malton (1818, 1820 & 1830)

Died unmarried 29 January 1871 (HM)

Agar, Seth

Clock and Watchmaker

Son of Richard Agar, pinner and hosier, baptised 5 May 1717 Holy Trinity, King's Court (PReg)

Clock and watchmaker, Free by patrimony 1744 (SS102/263)

Of Coney Street (YkCo 2 February 1748)

Household goods for sale (YkCo 10 September 1748)

House and shop near Black Swan, Coney Street, to be let [moved to Whitby] (YkCo 2 July 1751)

Agar, Thomas

Baptised 8 February 1758 Fulford (HM)

Apprenticed to his father, John Agar, watchmaker (q.v.), indenture 24 February 1774, 7 years (YCA D14/149)

Taken into partnership by his father (YH 12 November 1791)

Watchmaker, Free 1799 (Malden)

Councillor, Walmgate Ward (YH 26 September 1801)

Died 19 April buried St Olaves 24 April 1807 aged 49 (YkCo 20 April 1807, PReg)

Watchmaker of Pavement, succeeded by his nephew, Francis Agar, watchmaker (q.v.) (YkCo 4 May 1807)

Aire, Thomas

Goldsmith, Free 1659 (SS102/122)

Aitken, Thomas Quick
Son of William Aitken of York, bookbinder, apprenticed to James Barber (q.v.), George Cattle (q.v.) and William North (q.v.), jewellers, indenture 22 September 1832, 7 years (YCA D16/319)
Jeweller of Skeldergate, Free 31 May 1841 (Malden)

Alburwyk, Thomas
Goldsmith, Free 1401 (SS96/102)

Alexander
The goldsmith
Witness to a grant of land in Fossgate 1214x1216 (YASRS148/58)

Alne, Thomas de
Goldsmith, witness to a grant of land in Walmgate, 13 June 1304 (BTC16/106)

Alne, Walter de
Goldsmith
Witness to a grant of land in Patrickpool, 22 August 1250 (YASRS148/208)
Witness to a grant of land in Petergate, January 1252 (YASRS148/226)
Witness to grants of land in Stonegate, 1253x1261 (YASRS148/226), 1256 (YASRS148/268)

Alnwyck, Alan de
Goldsmith, Free 1350 (SS96/43)
Witness to a grant, 1355 (SRJ/1483)
Will 3 September proved 13 September 1374, left to his wife, Matilda, all his messuage in Stonegate and to his kinsman, William, the tools of the craft when he reaches age of 20 and is well schooled in the goldsmith's craft. Legacy to his mother, Emma, living in Alnwick. To be buried in the choir of St Michael le Belfrey where he used to sit or in the church of St Leonard's Hospital. Executor and legatee wife, Matilda. Left a silver spoon (SS4/91 & 92, YASRS38/2 & YWCWG)
Will of Matilda (Maud) de Alnwyck 20 February 1375 proved 20 June 1376 (YASRS38/2) To be buried in St Michael le Belfrey near her husband if there was room otherwise in York Minster before the altar of St John the Baptist. Requested that a chantry (one of six) be founded at the altar of St Thomas the Martyr in York Minster (NW side of NW pillar of the central tower) for the souls of herself and her husband to be endowed by two tenements in Petergate and Stonegate. Left four silver spoons, a silver piece called 'le collock', and a silver goblet. Her wishes carried into effect by John de Beverley, draper, 19 March 1376 (SS35/303, YWCWG)

Andrew, John (Andrewe)
Goldsmith, Free 1451 (SS96/171)
Witness to the will, 2 August 1467, of William Rotherham (q.v.), goldsmith (YWCWG)
Legatee of the will, 27 September 1469, of John Rode (q.v.), goldsmith (YWCWG)
For repairing 2 holywater vessels, 2 candelabra, and 1 reliquary in York Minster, 3s, 1469/70 (SS35/73)

17

For repairing a thurible, an image of the Virgin Mary, a water sprinkler and the shrine of St William, 8s, 1470/1 (SS35/76)

For repairing a thurible and a phial, 2s, 1472 (SS35/79)

For repairing a thurible, a chalice and a phial and also the shrine of St William, 7s 6d, 1473 (SS35/82)

Will 10 August proved 14 August 1477, to be buried in the ambulatory leading to the high choir in St Helen, Stonegate. Legatee wife Isabella (YASRS38/2, YWCWG)

Andrew, Peter (Androwe)

Goldsmith, Free 1474 (SS96/194)

Debt of 40d pending on chamberlains' accounts, payable to William Couke, sergeant at mace, 29 September 1476. Still pending, payable to [illegible], sergeant at mace, 30 November 1476. Still pending, payable to Richard Burgges, sergeant at mace, 3 February 1476. Not settled (Attreed/20, 24, 92 & 93)

Appilton, Thomas

Goldsmith, Free 1414 (SS96/119)

Appilton, William

Goldsmith, Free by patrimony 1422, son of William Appilton, barber (SS96/132)

Arleham, see Harlham

Armstrong, John

Son of John Armstrong, bricklayer, apprenticed to Charles Waggitt (q.v.), clock and watchmaker, indenture 4 June 1829, 7 years (YCA D16/246)

Of St John, Ouse Bridge, parish, married Teresa Hurworth 4 September 1836 St Mary Bishophill Junior (YG 10 September 1836 & PReg)

Clock and watchmaker, Free 28 April 1842 (Malden)

Commenced business at 164 Walmgate (YG 15 March 1845)

Removed to 188 Foss Bridge (YG 21 November 1857)

Watchmaker, died 9 June 1875 aged 60 buried York Cemetery grave 9176 apoplexy (YCReg)

Widow, Teresa, died 26 November 1880 (YG 27 November 1880)

Arnaldo

Goldsmith

For repairing the great cross and altar cross in York Minster, 7s 4d, 1507/8 (SS35/94)

For repairing various things and a jewelled appurtenance in York Minster, 4s 10d, 1509/10 (SS35/95)

Arscot, John van

Goldsmith, Free 1439 (SS96/154)

Arundel, John Cundall

Born 4 June 1816 (YG 2 September 1893) baptised 23 June 1816 Little Blake Street (RC) Chapel (PReg)

Watchmaker, son of Thomas Arundel, Glover, Free by patrimony 30 July 1839 (Malden)

Commenced business 1840 (YG 2 September 1893)

Of 67 Goodramgate (Dir 1849) 40 Goodramgate (Dir 1851)

Watchmaker, jeweller removed from 40 Goodramgate to 22 Coney Street (YG 17 Sept 1859)

Presented a biscuit box to be competed for by all members of 1st East Yorkshire Artillery in a shooting competition (YG 5 December 1885)

Competition won by Gunner Thornton (YG 12 December 1885)

Died 27 August 1893 aged 77 buried York Cemetery grave 1405, natural decay (YCReg)

Business continued by his wife, [Ellen] (*York Illustrated* (1895)/24)

Askwith, John

Watchmaker, son of Joseph Askwith, Free by patrimony 1741 (SS102/257)

Of Ousebridge, married Martha Townsend 1742 Aughton (Loomes/41)

Watchmaker of Spurriergate 1741, of Ousebridge 1758 (Poll)

Aspinall, James

Son of James Aspinall of St Martin, Coney Street, parish, glover, apprenticed to William Watson (q.v.), watchmaker, indenture 17 Dec 1818, 7 years, consideration £10 (YCA D16/32)

Astley, William

Son of Christopher Astley of Selby, Customs Officer, apprenticed to Richard Clark (q.v.), 7 years, 27 November 1777 (YCA D15/174)

Goldsmith, Free 1784 (Malden)

Working jeweller, gold and silversmith of Spurriergate, succeeded Richard Clark (q.v.) to whom he had been apprentice and journeyman (YH 8 April 1797)

Married Susanna Clark (YH 12 May 1798)

Assays at York 1807–21 (YAJ49/124–5)

Messuage in Spurriergate occupied by William Astley for sale (YkCo 14 December 1812)

Carried on business next door to former premises (YkCo 1 November 1813)

Father of William Astley, printer, Free by patrimony 1820 (Malden)

Working jeweller, Low Jubbergate (Dir 1823)

Father of John Astley, hatter, Free by patrimony 1830 (Malden)

Died, aged 73 (YG 8 June 1833)

His widow died 25 April 1848 aged 71 MI St Mary, Castlegate (YG 29 April 1848)

Atkinson, Jonathan

Goldsmith, son of George Atkinson, currier, Free by patrimony 1736 (SS102/243)

Atkinson, Thomas

Known in 1420 (Jackson/296)

Aughoo, John (Augo) (Jamin)

Goldsmith, Free 1368 (SS96/65)

Living with John Pinchbeck (q.v.) and others in a tenement in Stonegate between the tenements of the prebends of Barneby and Bilton and extending in length from the high street to the tenement of the prebend of Masham 4 October 1392 (SS186/25)

Left a knopped gold ring in the will of Joanna de Harlam wife of

Warymebolt de Harlam (q.v.) 1401 (SS4/282)
Elected searcher 27 August 1404 (SS120/248)
Will proved 10 January 1413 (YASRS38/3)
See also Jonyn

Austyn, Thomas
Goldsmith, Free 1491, 10s, part of fee, still owed (SS96/216)

Bagot, Robert
Goldsmith, Free 1453 (SS96/173)
Mentioned in connection with a debt of 12d in the inventory of William
Gale of York, April 1472 (YML Add MS L1/17/39)

Baines, Henry
Son of John Baines of York, apprenticed to William Whitwell (q.v.) and
James Barber (q.v.), jewellers, indenture 6 Oct 1821, 7 years (YCA
D16/82)
Engraver and silverchaser, Free 1830 (YCA D5)

Ballorini, Peter
In partnership with Phillip Cattaneo (q.v.) as Cataneo & Co. (YG 7
October 1848)

Banes, William
Goldsmith, Free 1479 (SS96/201)

Bankes, Thomas (Banks)
Goldsmith, Free 1553 (SS96/274), born Whixley (YAJ57/121)
Fined 2s 6d by the two wardens of the London company during their
searches in the north, 5 February 1561 (LGC minute book K/176)
Buried 20 August 1572 St Martin cum Gregory (PReg)

Barber, James *
Only surviving son of John Barber, [cabinet maker (RHS)] and toyman,
born 4 baptised 6 October 1784 Little Blake Street (R.C.) Chapel
Apprentice to John Hampston (q.v.), John Prince (q.v.), Robert Cattle
(q.v.) and George Cattle (q.v.), goldsmiths etc., indenture 21 March 1800,
7 years (PRO)
Taken into partnership by Robert Cattle (q.v.) after working 8 years in his
shop 1 January 1808 (YG 4 January 1808)
Jeweller, son of John Barber, gentleman (Free as a joiner 1784), Free by
patrimony [30 June] 1814 (Malden)
Partnership with Robert Cattle dissolved 1 January 1814 and new
partnership with William Whitwell (q.v.) formed (YkCo 24 October 1814)
Married Margaret Clark of the Black Swan, widow, 10 April 1814 St
Martin, Coney Street (PReg and YkCo 11 April 1814)
Coach–master Black Swan General Coach Office (YG 26 June 1819)
On death of William Whitwell (q.v.) in April 1823 new partnership formed
with George Dalby Cattle (q.v.) and William North (q.v.), premises 25
Coney Street (Dir 1830)
Sheriff 1826/7, Alderman 5 September 1832, Lord Mayor 1833, fined for
Lord Mayor 1844, re–elected Alderman 9 November 1847 (RHS) resigned
November 1853 (YG 12 November 1853)
Partnership dissolved 12 July 1847 (YG 24 July 1847)

Prime Warden, Goldsmiths' Company of York 1851 (YAJ49/117)

Died at Tang Hall, Heworth, 10 March 1857 aged 73 (YG 14 March 1857)

MI and Window Osbaldwick Church

Business to be carried on by his son, James Silburn Barber (q.v.) (YG 11 April 1857)

Barber, James Silburn

Born 15 baptised 20 February 1815 St Martin, Coney Street (PReg)

Of Osbaldwick, educated Mr Green's school, Ledsham 10 August 1829 – June 1832 (RHS)

To carry on the business at 25/26 Coney Street (YG 11 April 1857)

Old established gold, silver, and watch making business to be disposed of (YG 24 July 1858)

Business closed, notice to debtors (YG 12 March 1859)

Auction to sell premises (YG 6 July 1859), purchased by Robert Heselgrave (q.v.) and Robert Walker (q.v.), former employees of James Barber (q.v.) (Gubbins/19)

Free by patrimony 21 March 1866 (Malden)

Died 30 December 1884 at The Cottage, Osbaldwick, aged 68 (YG 5 January 1884)

Barbour, William

see Newton, William

Bardisman, Richard (Bardismore)

Goldsmith of York, purchased from Dean and Chapter of York the silver gilt reliquary that held the head of St William, 294 oz at 3s 10d an oz – £56 7s: gold 4 oz at 40s an oz – £8 10s : Total £68 17s 24 October 1541 (YAJ35/392)

Bargeman, John

Goldsmith, Free 1547 (SS96/267)

Fined 2s 6d by the two wardens of the London company during their searches in the north, 5 February 1561 (LGC minute book K/176)

Father of Thomas Bargeman, haberdasher, Free by patrimony 1589 (SS102/31)

Bargeman, Richard

Goldsmith, Free 1535 (SS96/254), born Wilberfoss (YAJ57/119)

Chamberlain 1547 (SS96/267)

Married Elizabeth, sister of John Lund (q.v.) (Reg. Test. 15/3 f132b)

Purchase a pyx from St Michael, Spurriergate, which had been stolen from the church by Thomas Dixon (q.v.), goldsmith, January 1547–January 1548 (StMSp 3/24b)

Witness to the will of Oswald Chapman (q.v.) (YWCWG)

Witness to the will of John Lund (q.v.) who bequeathed him a pair of boots with spurs, 10 August 1588 (Reg. Test 15/3 132b)

Father of George Bargeman, draper, Free by patrimony 1576 (SS102/17)

Bargeman, Roger

Goldsmith, Free 1616 (SS102/65)

Buried 27 February 1617 St Martin, Coney Street (PReg)

Will 26 February proved 13 March 1617, to be buried at the pleasure of his family. Executors, his mother, Merrel Wesbecke (possibly wife of Arthur Wesbecke, a witness) and his sisters, Ann and Joan Bargeman and Barbara Allanson (YASRS28/7, YWCWG)

Barnett, Henry Mark

Born and baptised 17 May 1832 Little Blake Street (R.C.) Chapel (PReg)
Son of Henry Mark Barnett of York, glass stainer, apprentice to John Bell (q.v.), jeweller, 7 years, 1 Jan 1846 (YCA D16/447)
Released from apprenticeship and attended York School of Design, glass painter of Tynemouth (HM)

Barri, John

Goldsmith, Free 1312 (SS96/14)

Barry, Robert

Goldsmith, Chamberlain 1350 (SS96/42), Bailiff 1365/6 living 1372 (RHS)
Ellen Barry, relict of Robert Barry, will proved 18 October 1401 (YASRS6/11)

Bartindale, Robert

Son of John Bartindale of Malton, Innkeeper, apprenticed to Grace Fryer (q.v.), clock and watchmaker, indenture 16 March 1826, 7 years, consideration £11 5s (YCA D16/129)

Bartliff, Charles

Baptised 6 May 1811, St Michael, New Malton, son of Robert Bartliffe (q.v.) and Charlotte (PReg)
Jeweller and watchmaker, 54 Coney Street (Dir 1843)
Stock and share broker, 53 Coney Street (YG 19 April 1845)
Jeweller and watchmaker, 53 Coney Street (Dir 1846)

Bartliff, George

Baptised 2 May 1779 Stockton in the Forest (PReg)
Watchmaker of Malton, son of George Bartliff of York, husbandman, [by his first wife] Free by patrimony [30 December] 1801 (YCA D4)
Of Malton 1807, 1818 (Poll)
Of Yorkersgate, Malton 1822–40 (Loomes/45)
Died 1846 aged 69 (Dinsdale/43)

Bartliff, Robert (Bartcliffe)

Born 1 baptised 6 December 1783 St Laurence (PReg)
Clock and Watchmaker of Malton, [first] son of George Bartliff of York, husbandman, [by his second wife] Free by patrimony 1807 (YCA D4)
Of Malton 1818, 1820 & 1830 (Poll)
Father of Williamson Bartliff of Malton, farmer, Free by patrimony 1829 (YCA D5)
Father of George Bartliff of Malton, surgeon, Free by patrimony 1830 (YCA D5)
Father of Charles Bartliff of York, spirit merchant, Free by patrimony 17 May 1838 (YCA D5)
Died 8 March 1855 aged 71 (Loomes/46)

Barton, Edward

Goldsmith, son of William Barton, Free by patrimony 1517 (SS96/239)
Of St Crux parish, paid lay subsidy of 5s 0d on goods of £10, 1524

(YAJ4/180)
Will 14 November 1528 proved 26 February 1528, to be buried in churchyard of St Crux. Executor and legatee wife, Barbara (YASRS11/12, YWCWG)

Basset, Jean Jacques Louis
Watchmaker of York
Of Holy Trinity, King's Court, parish, married there Mary Lavalette of St Saviour parish 20 August 1767 (PReg)
Of St Michael le Belfrey parish, son, John, buried there 22 March 1772 (PReg)

Bastard, Richard
Goldsmith, son of Henry Bastard of Thorparche, Free by patrimony 1335 (SS96/29)

Beckwith
see also Bekwith, Bekwyth

Beckwith, Ambrose, I (senior)
Son of Malby Beckwith, jeweller, apprentice to Valentine Nicholson (q.v.), indenture 6 September 1740, 7 years (YCA D13/71b)
Came from London and opened business in the premises of Mr Baker, Coney Street (YkCo 20 September 1748)
Free by order 1749 (SS102/268) goldsmith, admitted on payment of £25, 18 December 1749 (YCA B43/325)
At Tea Kettle and Lamp, next door to Black Swan in Coney Street, took John Malton (q.v.) into partnership (YkCo 19 December 1749)
Married Hannah Rhodes, both of Minster Yard, 18 Sept 1754 St Michael le Belfrey (PReg)
Partnership with John Malton dissolved April 1761, Ambrose Beckwith set up on his own at Golden Cup in Coney Street (Gubbins/11)
Insured with Sun Fire Office 1761 (LGC letter 11 November 1997)
Councillor Bootham Ward (YkCo 23 March 1762) until his death
Chamberlain 29 Jan 1768 (YCA B44/229)
Died 28 September 1770 aged 43 (YkCo 2 October 1770) MI St Maurice
Mrs Beckwith sold the business to John Hampston (q.v.) and John Prince (q.v.), journeyman and apprentice respectively with Ambrose Beckwith (q.v.) (YkCo 20 November 1770)

Beckwith, Ambrose, II
Came from London in late 1750s and was employed by Ambrose Beckwith I in his jewellery branch for upwards of 5 years until 1765 when he started his own business at the Crown and Pearl, Bedern Gate, Goodramgate (YkCo 22 January 1765)
Moved to Crown and Pearl, Coney Street (YkCo 23 July 1765)
Jeweller and goldsmith, Free by order 1766 (YCA D4) Working Jeweller admitted on payment of £20, 30 September 1766 (YCA B44/214)
Elected Councillor Bootham Ward 1 Oct 1767 (YCA B44/225)
Bankrupt, all stock sold (YkCo 24 January 1769, 16 Jan 1770)
Awarded £25 from Sir Thomas White's Gift by his fellow Councillors 27 June 1769 (YCA B44/253)

Back in business at the Crown and Pearl (YkCo 20 August 1771)

Removes to shop opposite the George in Coney Street (YkCo 18 August 1772)

Summoned to appear before the magistrates for deserting his apprentice, Timothy Platt (q.v.) 1776 (Gubbins/12 and 56)

Resigned as Councillor of Bootham Ward, letter of 18 Nov 1779 from Newcastle upon Tyne, resignation accepted 5 Jan 1780 (YCA B44/474, YkCo 18 January 1780)

Buried at St Andrew's, Newcastle, 16 July 1781 (Gill/58)

Beckwith, Charles
Jeweller, father of Malby Beckwith (q.v.), jeweller, flourishing in 1690s (Gubbins/11)

Beckwith, James
Free as a locksmith (?) 1623 (SS102/72)

Goldsmith, to answer information laid against him, November 1627. He had spoken 'divers prophane impious and scandalous wordes against the Church of England and the religion established therein'. Fined £20 and sentenced to stand, with a paper on his forehead inscribed in capital letters with his crime, on some barrel or hogshead from 10 a.m. to 11 a.m. in the Castle yard on Tuesday in the next Assize Week and the same hours in Pavement on the following Thursday, June 1628 (Aveling/238–9)

Recusant St Michael, Spurriergate, 1637, St Mary, Castlegate, 1640 (Aveling/240 & 241)

Wife, Katherine, buried 10 January 1642, St Mary, Castlegate (PReg)

Recusant, with wife Anne, of Nether Poppleton, 16 October 1657 (Aveling/243) She was a widow in 1681 (Aveling/254)

Beckwith, Malby
Jeweller, son of Charles Beckwith (q.v.), jeweller (Gubbins/11)

Baptised 30 January 1700 St Michael le Belfrey

Married first, Alice, daughter of John Abbu, mother of Ambrose Beckwith senior. (RHS)

Alice died 6 November 1735 aged 36 (MI St Maurice)

Married second Hannah, relict of William Dawson, January 1735 (RHS)

Died 2 November 1742 aged 41 (MI St Maurice) will 30 July 1742 proved 29 March 1743 (RHS)

Bedall, Alan de
Goldsmith, Free 1397 (SS96/98)

Searcher 27 August 1404 (SS120/248) 1417/18 (SS120/247) 3 November 1420 (SS186/58)

Lessee, with wife Joan, of lands and tenements in Stonegate in parish of St Michael le Belfrey lying between the tenements of the prebendaries of Barneby and Ampleforth, in length from Stonegate to the tenement of the prebendary of Masham, 10 November 1428 (SS186/96)

Bee, John
Goldsmith, son of John Bee, pewterer, Free by patrimony 1567 (SS102/8)

Beeforth, John
Watchmaker, son of George Beeforth, merchant tailor, Free by patrimony

1680 (SS102/154)

Beeforth, Robert

Free as a locksmith, 1650 (SS102/109)

Clocksmith of York, agreed that he is to have £8 yearly for keeping the clock and chimes of the Minster, and he is to find all wire, oil and other materials, except woodwork, cables and bells at his own charge. To be paid in equal portions at Martinmas and Whitsuntide, 23 June 1658 (YCA B37/112b)

Robert Hudson (q.v.) to assist him to gather together all the materials of the old clock and chimes, 23 June 1658 (YCA B37/113)

Bekwith, Leonard (Beckwythe, Bekewith)

Legatee of his father, Robert Bekwith (q.v.), goldsmith who by his will, 9 June 1585, left him the tools of his occupation (YWCWG)

Goldsmith, son of Robert Bekwith (q.v.), goldsmith, Free by patrimony 1590 (SS102/34)

Buried 27 May 1592 St Michael le Belfrey (PReg)

Will 21 April proved 27 June 1592. Executor and legatee wife, Ellen. Property in Stonegate and a stable with two chambers and a garden in Swinegate (YASRS38/5, YWCWG)

Bekwith, Ralph (Bekwyth)

Inventory of stock in trade in premises in Stonegate 1503 (Raine/119)

Member of Corpus Christi Guild 1526 (SS57/207)

Goldsmith, Free 1528 (SS96/248)

Will 18 March 1541, to be buried in St Michael le Belfrey. His brother, William Bekwith, to have his lease from the king of the lately dissolved house called the White Friars, with all other houses and parcels. Other legatees, Leonard Bekwith, 'my good master', and Ambrose Bekwith. He left a widow, Anne and a son, Anthony (SS57/208, YASRS38/6, YWCWG)

Mentioned in a grant of land in St Andrewgate, lease made 20 April 1543 (*Letters and Papers, Foreign and Domestic* 18, Part 1/533)

Bekwith, Robert (Beckwith, Beckewithe) *1561–68

Goldsmith, Free 1546 (SS96/267)

Chamberlain 1558 (SS96/279)

Fined 8s by the two wardens of the London company during their searches in the north, 5 February 1561 (LGC minute book K/176)

Lessee of the first shop next to the Chapel on the north side and west end of the [Ouse] bridge, 8s 4d, 8 January 1566 (YCA B26/60b)

Daughter, Edith, baptised 31 August 1567 St Michael le Belfrey (PReg)

Rent of shop to be raised from 8s 4d to 10s 0d, 31 March 1569 (YCA B24/132)

Swore an oath of good workmanship and paid 1s to the London company during their searches in the north. Also paid 3s for the swearing of am oath by his apprentice John Ralets, 17 July 1573 (LGC minute book L/158–9)

Feoffee with others of property in Tockwith 5 November 1582 (SS186/290)

Buried St Michael le Belfrey 5 April 1585 aged *c.*60 (PReg)
Will 18 July 1584, codicil 4 April proved 3 August 1585 (YASRS38/5)
Legatees wife, Jane (to have tenement, garden and orchard between Davygate and Swinegate), sons Leonard (to have the tools of my occupation) and Thomas, daughter Elizabeth, wife of Bryan Daragon, Ellen, wife of James Busfield, glover, and Joan. 'Bryan Daragon to make quietness betwixte my wife and children' (YWCWG)
Father of Thomas Bekwith, pewterer, Free by patrimony 1589 (SS102/32)
Father of Leonard Bekwith (q.v.), goldsmith, Free by patrimony 1590 (SS102/34)

Bekwyth, Edward
Goldsmith, Free 1519 (SS96/241)
Of Stonegate, will proved 20 August 1520 (YASRS38/6)

Bell, John
Goldsmith, Free 1526 (SS/247)
Of Holy Trinity, Goodramgate, paid lay subsidy of 12d on goods of 40s, 1524 (YAJ4/184)

Bell, John *
Parent in law Thomas Sharp of Tollerton, Farmer, apprentice to Christopher Watson (q.v.), jeweller, indenture 25 January 1819, 7 years (YCA D16/33)
Jeweller of Low Ousegate 1830 (Poll)
Taken into partnership by his brother in law, Christopher Watson – Watson and Bell of Low Ousegate (YG 5 May 1832)
Watson retired, John Bell sole proprietor 1 April 1844 (Gubbins/21)

Silversmith, jeweller and watchmaker 17 Low Ousegate (YG 1 July 1848, 14 January 1854)
Assistant Warden, York Assay Office 1851 (YAJ49/117)
Death of wife, Anne, aged 48 (YG 2 May 1868)
Death 28 August 1868 aged 62 buried York Cemetery grave 18114, epileptic convulsions (YCReg)

26

Beningborough, Henry de (Benigburg)
Goldsmith and glover 1272 (BL Cotton Nero D3/79/3)
Goldsmith, witness to a grant 1272/3 (YASRS148/7)
Occupier of property in Spen Lane 1272, 1275, 1278 (BL Cotton Nero D3/79/2, 3 & 4)

Bentley, John
Silversmith, Apprentice to Michael Bentley (q.v.), goldsmith, Free 1725/6 (SS102/226, Malden)
(Boy) Bentley, apprenticeship registered, 2 Dec 1717 (YCA B41/181)

Bentley, Michael
Goldsmith, apprentice to Arthur Mangy (q.v.), goldsmith, Free 1713/4 (SS102/205, Malden)

Bentley, William
Goldsmith, son of Samuel Bentley, Carpenter, Free by patrimony 1713/4 (SS102/208)

Berdnay, John de
Goldsmith, Free 1399 (SS96/102)
Fined 13s 4d for making false silver 1445/6 (SS120/248)

Best, John *1702
Goldsmith, son of Marmaduke Best (q.v.), goldsmith (Free 1658), Free by patrimony 1695 (SS102/174)
Appeared before the court of the London company for selling substandard gold and silver wares. Ordered to pay 18s, the cost of the goods, and charges of 20s, 3 May 1700 (LGC Court Book 10/213)

Best, Marmaduke *1658–86
Goldsmith, son of John Best, tailor, Free by patrimony 1657 (SS102/120)
Paid Hearth Tax on 3 hearths in a house in St Michael, Spurriergate, parish, 1671 (Hearth/12)
Chamberlain 1675 (SS102/145)
Father of John Best (q.v.), Free by patrimony 1695 (SS102/174)

Bewe, John
Goldsmith, restored to the Freedom 1412. He paid 3s 4d because he was poor (SS96/116)

Bewe, John (Bue)
Servant of Ralph Emondson (q.v.), goldsmith, who paid 3s for his swearing an oath to the London company, 17 July 1573 (LGC Minute Book L/158–9)
Goldsmith, Free 1574 (SS102/15)
Chamberlain 1588 (SS102/29)

Bewe, William
Goldsmith, takes an apprentice, William Bisshop (q.v.) 1612 (YCA D12/34b)

Bewlay, John
Clockmaker of York
Chamberlain 1801 (RHS)

Biggin, Martin du
See Byggyn, Martin du

Bilclife, John (Bilclif, Bilcliffe)
Clockmaker, Free 1618 (SS102/67)
Clocksmith, Chamberlain 1627 (SS102/76)

Bilclife, John (Bilcliffe)
Clockmaker, son of John Bilclife (q.v.), clockmaker, Free by patrimony 1640 (SS102/93)

Bilclife, Robert (Bilcliffe)
Watch —— , Free 1628 (SS102/77)
Of St Helen, Stonegate, parish, will 27 October proved 4 December 1641 (RHS)

Bilclife, Robert (Bilcliffe)
Clockmaker, son of Robert Bilclife, Free by patrimony 1653 (SS102/115)

Bispham, Thomas
Goldsmith, Free 1450 (SS96/170)

Bisshop, William
Son of Robert Bisshop of Fulford, grassman, apprentice to William Bewe (q.v.) of York, goldsmith, 8 years, 3 February 1612 (YCA D12/34b)

Blackburn, John de
Goldsmith, Free 1461 (SS96/181)
Grantor, with his wife, Elizabeth, of messuages outside Micklegate Bar, which she had for the term of her life, to Robert Atkynson of Newark 13 October 1458 (SS125/219)

Blackburn, Thomas de
Goldsmith, Free 1356 (SS96/50)
Paid rent, with William Fox (q.v.), goldsmith, for a tenement opposite the Cross on Ouse bridge, 36s, 25 January 1376 (SS120/6)

Blackstone, William
Son of George Blackstone, apprentice to William Whitwell (q.v.) and James Barber (q.v.) jewellers, indenture 28 February 1818, 7 years (YCA D16/20)
Jeweller of Whitby 1830 (Poll)
Working Jeweller, late of York, death of wife Elizabeth at Whitby (YG 30 March 1867)
Jeweller of 44 Crag Street, Whitby (Dir 1872)

Blake, Thomas
Goldsmith, Free 1558 (SS96/278)
Father of William Blake (q.v.), goldsmith, Free by patrimony 1584 (SS102/27)

Blake, William (Blayke)
Apprenticed to Robert Bekwith (q.v.), goldsmith, who left him £12 in his will, 9 June 1585 (YWCWG)
Goldsmith, son of Thomas Blake (q.v.), goldsmith (Free 1558), Free by patrimony 1584 (SS102/27)

Blanshard, Joseph
Son of Henry Blanshard of Gate Fulford, apprenticed to John Armstrong (q.v.), watch and clockmaker, indenture 15 April 1856, 7 years (YCA D16/509)

Blenkensop, Robert
Jeweller, Free 1487 (SS96/212)

Blund, Henry
Goldsmith
Donor of 12d, rent from land in Hungate and Aldwark 1150x1220 (SRJ/1720)
Recipient of 4s 0d, rent from land in Hungate and Aldwark 1251x1271 (SRJ/1722)

Blunt, William le
Goldsmith, son of Henry le Blunt, citizen of York, made grant of land in Layerthorpe 1250x1299 (YASRS148/148)

Blythe, Matthew John
Son of John Blythe of Redeness Street, York, apprentice to George Cattle (q.v.), James Barber (q.v.) and William North (q.v.), jewellers, indenture 29 July 1835, 7 years (YCA D16/74)
Engraver, Free 31 July 1847 (Malden)

Boniman, Richard
Goldsmith, known in 1575 (Jackson/298)

Booth, G.B.
Jeweller of Messrs Booth of Selby, Assays at York 1806–10 (YAJ49/119)

Booth, William B.
Jeweller of Messrs Booth of Selby, Assays at York 1806 and 1808–11 (YAJ49/119)

Bosvile, John
Son of Charles Bosvile of Carlton, gentleman, apprentice to Henry Hindley (q.v.), clockmaker, indenture 20 May 1738, 8 years (YCA D13/65b)

Bowes, Thomas
Goldsmith, Free 1499 (SS96/223)

Bownas, George
Son of John Bownas of York, coach guard, apprenticed to Horatio Smith (q.v.), watchmaker, indenture 6 February 1826, 7 years (D16/175)

Bradshaw, John
Watchmaker of St Michael le Belfrey parish married Sarah Daniel of the same parish 3 October 1762 St Michael le Belfrey (PReg)

Bray, John
Goldbeater, Free 1367 (SS96/63)

Brerey, Richard
Goldsmith, Free 1535 (SS96/254)
Son of William Brerey of Menston (RHS) born Forest of Knaresborough (YAJ57/118)
Member, with his wife, of Corpus Christi Guild 1546 (SS57/235)
Chamberlain 1539 (SS96/258)
Sheriff of York 1555/6 (Drake/364)
During his year of office he was committed to ward for his disobedient behaviour and for using opprobrious and unfitting words against the Lord Mayor, 5 June 1556 (YCA B22/20b)
Father of John Brerey, victualler, Free by patrimony 1562 (SS102/5)

Breton, John
  Goldsmith, Free 1412 (SS96/116)
  Died 1474 (Jackson/296)
Brewer, Thomas
  Son of Richard Brewer of Hook, yeoman, deceased, apprenticed to Henry Hindley (q.v.), clockmaker, indenture 12 May 1736, 8 years (YCA D13/62)
Brice, Francis
  see Bryce, Francis
Brigges, George
  Apprenticed to George Kitchin (q.v.), goldsmith and legatee of his will, 13 July 1597 (YWCWG)
Bright, Thomas
  Goldsmith, Free 1412 (SS96/117)
  Paid 3s 2d for repairs to mayor's sword 1433 (SS192/17)
  Administration of the estate of his wife, Joan, granted 6 May 1434 (YASRS6/24)
  Administration of his estate granted 24 May 1452 (YASRS6/26)
Briskham, William
  Son of John Briskham of York, ostler, apprentice to James Barber (q.v.) and William Whitwell (q.v.), silversmiths, indenture 19 May 1821, 7 years, consideration £20(YCA D15/75)
Brogden, Joseph
  Baptised 1 October 1749 St Crux (PReg)
  Silversmith, son of Joseph Brogden, cordwainer (Free 1740), Free by patrimony 1774 (YCA D4)
  Married Dorothy Lambert 29 January 1775 Holy Trinity, Goodramgate (PReg)
  Silversmith and hardwareman, Fossgate 1784 (Poll)
  Fined 5s 0d for having short weights 1795
  Silversmith of Fossgate 1807 (Poll)
Brogden, Robert
  Apprenticed to Thomas Cullender, clockmaker, no indenture (Malden)
  Clockmaker, Free 1714 (SS102/205)
  Father of Robert Brogden, Free by patrimony 1740 (SS102/252)
  Clockmaker of Selby 1741 (Poll)
  Living in 1763 (Dinsdale/47)
Bromley, Thomas
  Son of Thomas Bromley of Selby, mariner, apprenticed to William Astley (q.v.), silversmith, indenture 18 July 1807, 7 years, consideration 15 gns (YCA D15/208)
Brown, Jacob
  Son of Sarah Brown of York, apprenticed to Robert Cattle (q.v.), silversmith, indenture 14 April 1814, 7 years (YCA D15/285)
Browne, Michael
  Yeoman of York, apprenticed to George Mungie (q.v.) of York, goldsmith, indenture 10 July 1652, 7 years (YCA D12/91)

Bruyle, Peter
Goldsmith, Free 1411 (SS96/114)
Bryce, Francis (Brice) *1639
Goldsmith, son of John Bryce, innholder, Free by patrimony 1635 (SS102/86)
Baptised 14 April 1612 St Martin, Coney Street (PReg)
Wife buried 11 August 1644 St Martin, Coney Street (PReg)
Chamberlain 1649 (SS102/106)
Buck, John
Son of John Buck, publican of York, apprenticed to Edward Jackson (q.v.), jeweller and silversmith, indenture 12 May 1818, 7 years (YCA D16/43)
Son , John, baptised 19 February 1827 Holy Trinity, King's Court (PReg)
Silversmith of Sheffield, Free 1830 (YCA D5)
Buckle, Joseph *1717–21
Apprenticed to John Langwith (q.v.), goldsmith (Malden)
Goldsmith, Free 1716 (SS102/212)
Silver assayed at Newcastle 1716–19 (Gill/68)
Of Stonegate (London Gazette 28/31 January 1721 p. 5025, YkCo 22 October 1734, 13 October 1741, 26 July 1748, 3 October 1749, 19 February 1754, 26 October 1756)
Insured with Sun Fire Office 1724–56 (LGC letter 11 November 1997)
Chamberlain 1726 (SS102/225)
Sheriff 1730 (YkCo 28 April 1761)
Bill for £32 1s 0d for making a gold box for the Earl of Carlisle's Freedom 20 October 1732 paid 30 April 1733 by York Corporation (YCA C98A)
Gentleman of Stonegate 1758 (Poll)
Died 23 April 1761 aged 71 buried St Helen, Stonegate, MI (wrongly dated 1760)
Will 7 November 1758 codicil 8 Sept 1760 proved 10 July 1761, administration granted to his daughter Elizabeth, widow of John Smith (RHS)
Widow, Elizabeth, solicits business for her son, Stephen Buckle (q.v.), at his shop in Spurriergate (YkCo 28 April 1761)
Stonegate premises taken by Butler Burton, Grocer of Blake Street (YkCo 9 June 1761)
Widow, Elizabeth, died 22 January 1776 (YCh 26 January 1776), administration of her estate granted November 1777 (RHS)
Buckle, Stephen *1747–48
Baptised 6 Sept 1717 St Helen, Stonegate (PReg)
Apprenticed to Isaac Cookson, goldsmith at the Gold Ring, Newcastle, indenture 27 April 1732, 7 years. Free of Newcastle by servitude 15 January 1738 (Gill 69)
Goldsmith, son of Joseph Buckle (q.v.), gentleman, Free by patrimony 1741 (SS102/258)
Silversmith of Stonegate 1741 (Poll)
Married Cawood 31 July 1744 Ann daughter of James Smith, gentleman,

of Cawood (RHS)

Chamberlain 1750 (SS102/269)

Insured with Sun Fire Office 1756–61 (LGC letter 11 November 1997)

Silversmith of Spurriergate 1758 (Poll)

Continued his father's business at his (Stephen Buckle's) shop in Spurriergate (YkCo 28 April 1761)

Sheriff 1764/5 (Wilson/140)

Retired and sold his shop to Richard Clark (q.v.), working goldsmith (YkCo 1 Feb. 1774)

Will 30 June 1768 codicil 24 August 1775 proved 20 March 1776, to be buried at Cawood (RHS)

Death of widow, Ann (YkCo 16 June 1789)

Buk, John

Goldsmith, Free 1441 (SS96/157)

Burrill, John

Son of Thomas Burrill, Butcher of York, apprenticed to John Prince (q.v.), Robert Cattle (q.v.) and George Cattle (q.v.), jewellers and silversmiths, indenture 10 September 1806, 7 years (YCA D15/197)

Silversmith, Free 3 September 1814 (YCA D5)

Silversmith of Bootham Square 1818 (Poll)

Silversmith of Micklegate (Dir 1823)

Silversmith of Colliergate 1830 (Poll)

Working silversmith of Barber and North, appointed assayer in place of Thomas Stead (q.v.) (YG 11 May 1839)

Father of John Burrill, junior, printer, Free by patrimony 17 July 1843 (Malden)

Silversmith, 70 Petergate (Dir 1846)

Worn out spoon maker in employ of Mr Barber 1851 (YAJ49/117)

Victualler, of Tiger Inn, 15 Jubbergate [now Market Street] (Dir 1851)

Of Charles Street, died 14 January 1864 aged 73 buried York Cemetery grave 4787 Pneumatic Gout (YCReg)

Death of widow, Jane, aged 75 (YG 16 May 1868)

Busfield, Hannah

Wife of William Busfield (q.v.), goldsmith, continued his business after his death in 1709.

Insured with Sun Fire Office 1724 (LGC letter 11 November 1997)

Buried 24 April 1728 St Martin, Coney Street (PReg)

Busfield, John

Baptised 27 November 1694 St Martin, Coney Street (PReg)

Goldsmith, son of William Busfield (q.v.), goldsmith (Free 1680), Free by patrimony 1727/28 (SS102/229)

Chamberlain 1731 (SS102/231)

Married Ann, daughter of Alderman James Dodsworth, mercer, 13 June 1731 St Sampson (PReg)

Bill of £32 13s 0d paid by York Corporation 27 April 1733 (YCA C98A)

12 Aug. 1732 For mending punch ladle, caster, marrow spoon, pair of snuffers and a stand 6s 0d

13 September	For making a gold box for the Freedom of the Earl of Burlington	£31 5s 0d
18 December	For 8 new blades and 1 fork and fixing in silver handles	10s 0d
23 December	For deepening, planishing and burnishing a soup dish, for mending a spoon	12s 0d

Goldsmith of Coney Street (YkCo 29 April 1729, 30 August 1743)

Declined business in favour of John Terry (q.v.), goldsmith (also watchmaker) (YkCo 24 May 1748)

Busfield, William *1674–1703

Goldsmith, son of Thomas Busfield, pewterer, Free by patrimony 1680 (SS102/153)

Married Hanna Carr of York 25 August 1685 York Minster (PReg)

Appeared before Mr Loftus of the London company for selling substandard gold and silver wares. Ordered to pay £5 8s, the costs of the goods, and charges of £6 6s, 23 August 1700 (LGC Court Book 10/220)

Buried 5 June 1709 St Martin, Coney Street (PReg) Business continued by wife, Hannah Busfield (q.v.)

Father of John Busfield (q.v.), goldsmith, Free by patrimony 1728 (SS102/229)

Bustard, John

Goldsmith, Free 1345 (SS96/38)

Byggyn, Martyn (Biggin, Dubiggyn, Doubiggon, Dowbiggyns)

Goldsmith, son of Robert Byggyn, cordwainer, Free by patrimony 1572 (SS102/13)

Swore an oath of good workmanship and paid 3s 4d to the London company during their searches in the north. A pile of his weights taken for sizing, 17 July 1573 (LGC minute book L/158–9)

Searcher, having abused himself towards the Lord Mayor, to be committed to ward in Monk Bar during the Lord Mayor's pleasure and to be discharged from his searchership and another honest person appointed in his place 22 March 1582 (YCA B28/94b) Replaced by Thomas Waddy (q.v.) (YCA B28/10)

As a result of divers suits, controversies, debates, complaints and demands between Martyn Byggyn and George Kitchin (q.v.), goldsmiths, an award of 50s was made in favour of Martyn Byggyn 23 September 1583 (YCA B28/114)

To be paid 9s 0d for every ounce of silver gilded on the city's great sword, about 20½ ounces, and 20s 0d for gilding the pommel of the sword 2 September 1586 (YCA B29/123b)

Buried 25 March 1602 St Michael le Belfrey (PReg)

Byngham, Thomas de

Goldbeater, Free 1371 (SS96/68)

Cadman, George

See Roberts, Samuel, junior

Camidge, John *1681

Goldsmith, 1660 (Jackson/298)

Campey, Joseph
Apprenticed to Henry Hindley (Malden) 1755 (Setchell/50)
Clockmaker, Free 1758 (SS102/281)

Carlill, James Bellamy
Son of a merchant of Marazion, Cornwall, apprenticed at age 12 to
William Pridgin (q.v.), watchmaker, indenture 16 September 1787, until
aged 21 (YCA D15/5)
Issued a ½d coin with a portrait of Constantine on it, 1796 (YEP 27 April
1983)
Watchmaker, Free 1801 (Malden)
Watchmaker and jeweller of Coney Street (YH 14 March 1801, 22 August
1801, YkCo 23 August 1802)
Chamberlain 1802 (RHS)
House etc., extending to the Ouse, for sale (YkCo 12 December 1805)
Of Fulford, notice to creditors (YkCo 24 February 1806)

Carliolo, Nicholaus de
Goldsmith, Free 1312 (SS96/13)

Cartwright, Thomas
Goldsmith, Free 1635 (SS102/89)

Carter, Willey E.
Apprenticed to Jonathan Storr (q.v.), watchmaker, indenture 11 Dec 1777,
7 years, consideration £25, tax of £1 5s paid 8 December 1784 (PRO)

Casson, Elizabeth
Widow of Sem Casson (q.v.)
Search of her shop made by two wardens of London company, 8 August
1635. Parcels of plate were removed which, upon assay on 10 August,
were found to be substandard. After melting down or defacing raw
material returned to her upon a fine and a pledge not to offend again (LGC
Minute Book Si/259–266)
Will 4 August 1646 proved December 1646 (RHS)

Casson, Sem (Casse) *1618–32
Goldsmith, Free 1614 (SS102/63)
Married Elizabeth Elstob 7 November 1614 St Michael le Belfrey (PReg)
Chamberlain 1630 (SS102/80)
Will 26 February 1633 proved 21 January 1634. Executor and legatee
wife, Elizabeth. Owner of a tenement in Micklegate (YASRS35/16,
YWCWG)
Father of Roger Casson (q.v.), goldsmith, Free by patrimony 1646
(SS102/103)
Buried 27 February 1633 St Michael le Belfrey in the high cross aisle
(PReg) Business continued by his wife, Elizabeth Casson (q.v.)

Casson, Robert *1607
Goldsmith, Free 1607 (SS102/54)
To have time until three weeks after Easter to make 'an hableinge piece of
worke' and in the meantime to have the benefit of Company of Goldsmiths'
touch and when the work is done to show it to the Lord Mayor to see if
it 'be workmanlie and artificiallie done' 12 March 1606 (YCA B33/60b)

Casson, Roger
Goldsmith, son of Sem Casson (q.v.), goldsmith (Free 1614), baptised 14 April 1622 (PReg) Free by patrimony 1646 (SS102/103)
Supervisor of his father's will, 26 February 1633 (YWCWG)
Will 9 June 1657, to be buried St Michael le Belfrey (YASRS49/18)
Buried 8 July 1657 St Michael le Belfrey at the high end of the middle aisle under the highest seat (PReg)
Cateby, John de
Goldsmith, Free 1386 (SS96/84)
Cattaneo, Austin
In partnership with Phillip Cattaneo (q.v.) and others as Cattaneo & Co (YG 7 October 1848)
Cattaneo, Henry
Witness at the marriage of Joseph Fattorini (q.v.) St Mary, Castlegate 30 January 1837 (PReg)
In partnership with Phillip Cattaneo (q.v.) and others as Cattaneo & Co (YG 7 October 1848)
Working jeweller, 2 St Martins Lane (Dir 1849, 1850, 1855)
Hawker, died 27 Feb 1860 aged 54 buried York Cemetery grave 14151 natural decay (YCReg)
Cattaneo, John
Watchmaker, High Petergate (Dir 1849)
In partnership with Phillip Cattaneo (q.v.) and others as Cattaneo & Co (YG 7 October 1848)
Cattaneo, Joseph
Watchmaker of London married Ann daughter of John Mouncer and widow of Robert Hodgson (q.v.), jeweller of Minstergates, who died 6 February 1844. Took over business of Robert Hodgson (HM)
Wife, Ann, died 1 May 1848 aged 31 buried York Cemetery grave 12455 with her first husband, consumption (YCReg)
House and shop at corner of Petergate at south entrance of Minster for sale (YG 3 June 1848)
Jeweller etc., assigns his effects in the case of Tomlinson v Cattaneo (YG 5 May 1849)
Insolvent debtor – petition for protection from process (YG 29 September 1849)
Watch and clockmaker, working jeweller and dealer in plate, Minstergates – insolvent debtor (YG 11 September 1852)
Cattaneo, Phillip
Insolvent debtor, licensed hawker and dealer in clocks, watches, jewellery, cutlery, barometers, etc., lodging at 30 Parliament Street, formerly of 12 Castlegate in partnership with Henry Cattaneo (q.v.) and Joseph Fattorini (q.v.) as Cattaneo & Co. formerly of King's Staithe carrying on the same business in partnership with Henry Cattaneo, Joseph Fattorini, Austin Cattaneo (q.v.), John Cattaneo (q.v.) and Peter Ballorini as Cattaneo and Co (YG 7 October 1848)
Licensed hawker of 30 Parliament Street, petition for protection from

process (YG 7 April 1849)

Hawker, died 27 November 1859 in Union Workhouse, buried York Cemetery aged 54 grave 14767 consumption (YCReg)

Cattel, William *

Goldsmith and working jeweller from London, takes over premises in Stonegate of R. Hardy, wigmaker, hairdresser, perfumer [died 1790] (YkCo 8 July 1811)

Jeweller, Free by order 1812 (Malden)

Assays at York 1816–21 (YAJ49/119)

House in Stonegate for sale (YG 3 November 1821)

Business taken over by Horatio Smith (q.v.), clock and watchmaker (YG 30 July 1825)

Died 3 March 1830 aged 56 buried in a vault at St Olaves, MI

Widow, Sarah, died 11 February 1842 aged 71 MI

Cattle, Barbara *

Only daughter of William Lee, antique dealer and wife of Ian Roy Dodgson (died 31 January 1960), partners in I & B Dodgson, silversmiths of 25 Stonegate.

Married, second, Robert Alexander Cattle (Lord Mayor 1962)

From 1 March 1962 firm known as Barbara Cattle, silversmith (YEP 7 March 1962)

Moves from 25 to 45 Stonegate (YEP 13 June 1963)

Registered her maker's mark, BC, with Birmingham Assay Office 22 June 1965 (letter from librarian at Birmingham Assay Office)

Registered her maker's mark, BC, with Sheffield Assay Office 26 March 1968 (letter from librarian at Sheffield Assay Office)

Designer of Racing Trophies (YEP 7 June 1968)

Business bought by Bright & Son of Scarborough, part of the H.L. Brown of Sheffield group (YEP 1 May 1969)

Cattle, George *

Baptised 1 April 1764 St John, Ousebridge, son of Joseph Cattle and Frances Hall (PReg)

Silversmith, son of Joseph Cattle, translator deceased, Free by patrimony 4 April 1785 (Malden)

In partnership with John Hampston (q.v.), John Prince (q.v.) and Robert Cattle (q.v.), jewellers, Coney Street c.1796 (HM)

Married Ann Priscilla Dalby of Acomb 19 September 1795 St Stephen's, Acomb (PReg)

Councillor, Bootham Ward (YkCo 7 March 1803, YCh 5 Oct 1807)

Died 29 Sept 1807 aged 43 buried St Stephen's, Acomb, brain fever (YkCo 5 October 1807)

Cattle, George Dalby *

Jeweller of Barber, Cattle and North of Coney Street

Taken into partnership by James Barber (q.v.) and William North (q.v.), jewellers, after death of William Whitwell (q.v.) in April 1823 (HM)

Married Mary Elizabeth, daughter of William Staveley and widow of William Whitwell 31 October 1824 St Martin, Coney Street (PReg)

Left firm between September 1835 and July 1836 (Gubbins/17)
Died at Scarborough 14 July 1838 aged 41 (YG 21 July 1838)
Widow, Mary, died February 1847 aged 52 (YG 27 February 1847)
Cattle, Robert *
Born in Sheriff Hutton, son of James and Hannah Cattle (HM)
Came to York c.1792 and taken into partnership, with George Cattle (q.v.), by John Hampston (q.v.) and John Prince (q.v.), jewellers, to form Hampston, Prince and Cattles c.1796 (HM)
Married Mary Brough 8 August 1795 St Martin, Coney Street (PReg)
Insured with Sun Fire Office 1796 (LGC letter 11 November 1997)
Silversmith, Free by order 1807 (Malden)
John Hampston died in 1805 and after partnership between John Prince and Robert Cattle was dissolved on 1 November 1807 he traded on his own as a goldsmith, jeweller, watchmaker and engraver (YkCo 9 November 1807) until 1 January 1808 when he took James Barber (q.v.), who had worked in the shop in Coney Street for 8 years, into partnership (YkCo 1 January 1808)
Assays at York 1807 (YAJ49/119)
Chamberlain 1809 (RHS)
After partnership with James Barber dissolved on 1 January 1814 (YkCo 24 October 1814) he started a new occupation in charge of mails and post horses at the stables next to the York Tavern in St Helen's Square. (Gubbins/15)
Sheriff 1816/7 (RHS)
Gentleman of Grove House 1818, 1820 & 1830 (Poll)
Mr Maddocks taken into partnership 1827 (YH 6 October 1924) as Cattle and Maddocks, coach proprietors, in charge of posting arrangements at the York Tavern, stables in Jubbergate (YG 2 May 1829)
Alderman 9 October 1838 (RHS)
Lord Mayor 1840 (RHS)
Died at Grove House 22 October 1842 aged 76 buried Sheriff Hutton MI
Widow, Mary, died at Whitwell aged 87 (YG 23 September 1848)
Caverd, Philip
Goldsmith, Free 1541 (SS96/261)
Cay, William
Son of Stephen Cay of Selby, factor, apprenticed to William Astley (q.v.), goldsmith, indenture 1 February 1802, 7 years (YCA D15/156)
Silversmith, Free 1809 (Malden)
Jeweller of Leeds 1818, of Selby 1820, of Hull 1830 (Poll)
Cayley, Richard (Kaley)
Jeweller of Stonegate, son, Richard, baptised 2 June 1741 St Olaves (PReg)
Jeweller, Free by order 1753 (SS102/272)
Jeweller, goldsmith of Coney Street (YkCo 26 March 1754)
Jeweller of Coney Street 1758 (Poll)
Chaunge, John del (Eschaunge)
Goldsmith, Free 1328 (SS96/24)

Will of wife Alice, 31 October 1330, no probate. Left a silver and a silver–gilded clasp (YASRS38/22)

Cayne, John
Goldbeater, Free 1342 (SS96/35)

Champney, Charles
Son of William Champney of York, apprenticed to John Smith (q.v.), clockmaker, indenture 20 Dec 1764, 8 years (YCA D14/77)

Chaumberlayn, John
Goldsmith, Free 1396 (SS96/96)

Chapman, Oswald
Goldsmith, Free 1532 (SS96/251)
Burial recorded in St Michael, Spurriergate, churchwardens accounts, January 1545–January 1546 (StMSp 3/18b)
Will 5 September proved 17 December 1546. Executor and legatee wife, Agnes. Witnesses Richard Bargeman (q.v.) and John Lunde (q.v.) (YASRS11/37, YWCWG)

Chapman, George *
Watchmaker and jeweller, formerly with George and T. Davison at Newcastle upon Tyne, took over business of George Frederick Heselwood (q.v.) at North End House, 51 Coney Street (YG 9 May 1885)
Watch and clockmaker, working goldsmith, jeweller and chaser, heraldic and general engraver (Dir 1887, 1895, 1896 and 1898)
Registered his mark (GC) as gold and silversmith and jeweller with Birmingham Assay Office 4 October 1897 (letter from librarian at Birmingham Assay Office)
Of 66 Holgate Road, died 5 December 1907 aged 58 buried York Cemetery grave 5893 (YCReg)
Widow, Jane, of 58 Millfield Road, died 7 January 1915 aged 70 buried York Cemetery grave 5893 (YCReg)

Chapman, Sidney
Pawnbroker and silversmith of Thorpe Street
Died 17 July 1887 aged 29 buried York Cemetery grave 891 phthisis (YCReg)

Chester, Hugh de (Cestria)
Goldsmith, witness to a grant 20 July 1278 (YASRS148/210)

Chester, John
Jeweller, Free 1444 (SS96/162)

Chester, William de
Goldsmith, Free 1335 (SS96/29)

Chewe, Richard *1682
Goldsmith, Free 1665 (SS102/129)
Paid Hearth Tax on 1 hearth in a house in St Michael, Spurriergate, parish, 1671 (Hearth/12)
Father of William Chewe, Free by patrimony 1698 (SS102/180)

Clareburgh, John
Paid £13 6s 8d for supplying a new clock for York Minster, complete with weights and bells, 1371 (SS35/10)

Locksmith, Free 1388 (SS96/86)

Clapott, Dennis
Watchmaker, Free 1698 (SS102/177)

Clarke, Charles alias De Coster (Clerke)
Goldsmith, Free 1604 (SS102/49)
14 February 1603/4 Charles Clarke, a stranger, recommended for the franchise by Edmund Sheffield, President of the Council of the North. Granted on payment of 20 marks of which 20 nobles were to be refunded and paid off at 13s 4d yearly at Pentecost (YCA B32/310)
Son, Christopher (q.v.), taken as an apprentice, 9 years, 1 November 1610 (YCA D12/52)
Search of his shop made by two wardens of London company, 8 August 1635. Parcels of plate were removed which, upon assay on 10 August, were found to be substandard. After melting down or defacing raw material returned to him upon a fine and a pledge not to offend again (LGC Minute Book Si/259–266)

Clarke, Christopher
Apprenticed to his father, Charles de Coster alias Clarke (q.v.), goldsmith, 9 years, 1 November 1610 (YCA D12/52)
Fined with father, Charles Clarke (q.v.), for selling substandard plate, 8 August 1635 (LGC Minute Book Si/259–266)

Clarke, George
Goldsmith, for trimming the city's great sword 15s 0d (Jewitt/450)

Clarke, Robert
Born 9 Baptised 22 July 1785 St Michael le Belfrey (PReg)
Watchmaker of London, son of Thomas Clarke, plumber and glazier [of Stonegate], deceased, Free by patrimony [18 June] 1807 (Malden)
Watchmaker of Stonegate, married Margaret, daughter of late Richard Clark (q.v.), silversmith (YkCo 25 January 1808)
Watchmaker of Hull 1818, of Cottingham 1820 (Poll)
Died 18 July 1820 aged 34 buried St Stephen's Acomb, MI (PReg)
Widow, Margaret, died in Dublin (YG 21 October 1843)

Clark[e], Richard *
Apprenticed to John Malton (q.v.), goldsmith, indenture 26 August 1760, 9 years (YCA D14/38)

Goldsmith, Free by order 1773 (Malden)
Purchases shop of Stephen Buckle (q.v.), goldsmith, Spurriergate (YkCo

1 February 1774)

Shop on the corner of Low Jubbergate (now Market Street) and Spurriergate, January 1782 (White)

Jeweller and silversmith, Spurriergate 1784 (Poll)

Elected Councillor, Walmgate Ward (YkCo 17 September 1784)

Requested immediately to make a gold box of 100 pounds value for the Freedom of the Duke of York 11 October 1787 (YCA B45/275). Bill of £101 11s 6d (including shagreen case at £1 11s 6d) submitted 12 December 1787 and authorised for payment 2 February 1788 (YCA C68 & 69)

To prepare a gold box for the Freedom of the Duke of Clarence 30 August 1789 (YCA B45/351)

Died 13 March 1797 aged 50 (YH 18 March 1797) MI St Michael, Spurriergate

Widow, Elizabeth, transferred business to William Astley (q.v.), who had been his apprentice and journeyman (YkCo 8 April 1797)

She died at Gainsborough (YkCo 16 November 1812)

Clarke, Thomas

Goldsmith, son of Christopher Clarke (Free 1610), Free by patrimony 1651 (SS102/111)

Clark[e], William

Son of Marmaduke Clarke of York, dyer, apprenticed to Henry Hindley, clockmaker, indenture 29 June 1748, 7 years (YCA D13/123b)

Clockmaker, Free 1758 (Malden)

Clockmaker of Minster Yard 1758 (Poll)

Set up on his own as a clock and watchmaker in Low Ousegate (YkCo 11 August 1761) next door to Fortune of War public house (Loomes/64)

Took William Vincent (q.v.) into partnership, partnership dissolved 1764 (YkCo 7 August 1764)

Elected Councillor, Walmgate Ward (YkCo 7 October 1766)

Two dozen silver table spoons ordered for Mansion House, 26 January 1776, bill submitted for £19 10s (Gubbins/24)

Chamberlain 1778 (RHS)

Married Frances, daughter and coheir of Alderman Francis Stephenson 5 August 1779 (YkCo 10 August 1779)

Father of Sir William Stephenson Clarke (RHS)

Trustee, with John Holmes (q.v.), John Smeaton and 2 others in York Waterworks; owned 3 shares of £250 each (out of 28), 12 October 1779 (Radley/151)

Recommended, with John Hampston (q.v.) and John Prince (q.v.), to repair silver plate in the Mansion House, 25 February 1780 (YCA B45/12)

Sheriff 1786/7 (Wilson/140)

Purchased a further share in York Waterworks from John Smeaton for £400, 1788 (Radley/151)

To make 100 guinea gold box for the Freedom of the Prince of Wales, 20 July 1789 (YCA B45/351)

Died 13 February 1796 aged 61 buried St Michael, Spurriergate MI

Widow died 15 June 1819 in parish of St Helen, Stonegate, MI St Michael, Spurriergate, will proved 10 August 1819 (RHS)

Clayton, Robert
Goldsmith, Free 1641 (SS102/95)

Cleseby, Richard de
Goldsmith, Free 1387 (SS96/84)
Elected searcher, 27 August 1404 (SS120/248)
Late holder of a tenement in North Street together with rooms and other houses built there, rent 46s 8d per annum, 21 June 1418 (SS186/56)

Clifton, Walter de
Goldsmith, witness to a document 1200x1300 (SRJ/1657)

Cloak, Edward
Son of James Cloak, carver, gilder and looking glass manufacturer, apprenticed to James Barber (q.v.) and William North (q.v.), silversmiths and jewellers, indenture 4 February 1837, 7 years (YCA D16/432)
Silversmith, Free 15 July 1846 (Malden)
Shopkeeper of Layerthorpe, died 23 September 1865 aged 43 buried York Cemetery grave 7523 disease of heart (YCReg, YG 30 September 1865)

Close, John (Closse)
Goldsmith, Free 1417 (SS96/125)
Member, with his wife Cibella, of Corpus Christi Guild, 1432 (SS57/32)
Will 4 May proved 17 September 1442, to be buried St John's, Ousebridge. Executor and legatee wife, Sibyl (YASRS6/39, YWCWG)

Clyff, Thomas de
Goldsmith 1377 (SS96/74)

Clyveland, John de (Cleveland)
Goldsmith, Free 1394 (SS96/94)
Searcher 5 March 1410 (SS120/75)
Tenement in Stonegate, once in his possession but now occupied by Henry Forester (q.v.), goldsmith, rent paid £4 per annum, 11 March 1421 (SS120/75)

Coates, George
Son of Joseph Coates of Leeds, Dyer, apprenticed to Christopher Watson (q.v.), jeweller, 7 years, 23 May 1827 (YCA D16/199)

Cobb, William
Watchmaker, son of William Cobb, girdler, Free by patrimony 1659 (SS102/123)
Wife, Anne, buried 19 July 1673 St Michael le Belfrey (PReg)

Cockfield, William
Goldsmith, son of George Cockfield, chamber valet to Lord Lescrop [Scrope], Free by patrimony 1482 (SS94/204)
William Cokfeld de Cokfeld de Ebor, under bond of £10 to keep the peace, 9 March 1484 (Attreed/428)
Of St Michael le Belfrey parish, goldsmith, administration of estate granted 5 October 1485 (YASRS38/15)

Colayne, Herman
Son of John Colayne (q.v.)

Executor of his father's will, 28 July 1490, recipient of a bequest of a 'lanteryn' with balance, all the tools in the workshop and his father's saddle and 'gonstaff' (SS53/56, YWCWG) Received residuary portion of his father's estate, £3 18 2d (Reg Test I/354a)

Colayne, John (Colam, Colan, Culayn, Cullan)

Goldsmith, Free 1449 (SS96/169)

Legatee of the will, 27 September 1469, of John Rode (q.v.), goldsmith (YWCWG)

For making the weather vanes for new bell tower at York Minster and providing gold for them, a part of 8s 8d, 1485 (see William Webb) (SS35/88)

For mending the large gold cross at York Minster, 20d, 1485 (SS35/89)

Father of John Colayne, painter, Free by patrimony 1489 (SS96/213)

Will 28 July 1490 proved 7 August 1490 (YASRS38/15) To be buried at St Michael le Belfrey in the place where his [first] wife, Agnes, laid. Executor and legatee second wife, Agnes (SS53/56, YWCWG)

Inventory appraised 12 August 1490 – 7s owed to the prior and convent of St Oswald [Nostell] for rent of his house [in Stonegate]. His wife's residuary portion of her husband's estate £3 18 2d (Reg Test I/354a)

Colayne, Nicholas

Goldsmith, Free 1441 (SS96/157)

Fined 20s for selling articles of silver mixed with copper 1445/6 (SS120/247–8)

Colburn, John

Born 20 January 1826 (YG 19 May 1877)

Pawnbroker (YG 28 November 1846)

Married Jane only daughter of William Horsley of Wigginton, yeoman (YG 12 February 1848)

Jeweller, pawnbroker, silversmith, clothier and general dealer, 13 and 14 Low Ousegate, behind St Michael, Spurriergate church (YG 1 October 1853)

11 and 12 Church Lane (YG 15 November 1856)

Lord Mayor 1869 (RHS)

Silversmith and jeweller 13 Low Ousegate (Dir 1876)

Of Mount Villa, Dringhouses, died 17 May 1877 aged 51 at Boulogne buried York Cemetery grave 5932 MI dropsy (YCReg)

Collingwood, Robert

Son of John Collingwood of Rochdale, Lancashire, apprentice to William Fryer, clock and watchmaker, indenture 22 May 1820, 7 years, consideration £29 (YCA D16/55)

Collins, John

Apprentice to William Darling, watchmaker and jeweller, indenture 11 April 1835, 7 years (YCA D16/361)

Lived with his mother and stepfather, Mr and Mrs Brown, in Micklegate, committed suicide (YG 24 May 1851)

Died 22 May 1851 aged 29 buried York Cemetery grave 4413 accidental death (YCReg)

Colonia, John de
Goldsmith, Free 1367 (SS96/63)
Colonia, John de
Goldsmith, Free 1389 (SS96/87)
Colonia, John de
Goldsmith, Free 1398 (SS96/100)
Colonia, Sibtus
Goldsmith, Free 1397 (SS96/98)
Colton, William
Goldsmith, son of William Colton, corn merchant, Free by patrimony 1570 (SS102/11)
Father of Edward Colton, tailor, Free by patrimony 1600 (SS102/44)
Father of John Colton. pinner, Free by patrimony 1602 (SS102/47)
Conder, James Duke
Apprentice to William Darling (q.v.), watchmaker and jeweller, indenture 12 July 1854, 7 years (YCA D16/502)
Connold, William Henri
Jeweller married Priscilla youngest daughter of Daniel Ebbetto of London (YG 12 March 1853)
Watchmaker, jeweller and silversmith commenced business at 25 Spurriergate (YG 15 July 1854)
Sale of whole stock in trade (YG 7 May 1864)
Constance, Thomas
See Custance, Thomas
Cook, William
Goldsmith, Free 1487 (SS96/213)
Cook[e], Lewis
Clockmaker, Free 1615 (SS102/64)
Although not a freeman of York he was allowed, as he was a perfect and skilful workman in his art, to work privately in the city until Pentecost [Whit Sunday] 30 January 1614 (YCA B34/50b)
His licence to work extended until mid–summer when further consideration would be given to his admission to the franchise, 26 April 1615 (YCA B34/59b)
Very skilful in his art or science, admitted to the freedom without charge on condition that he gave a clock of his own manufacture to the value of 26 nobles to the Corporation before St Andrews day next [30 November] which he is to maintain for life. He was to become bound, with Lancelot Turner, that neither he nor his children would become a charge on the city for their relief or maintenance, 7 July 1615 (YCA B34/64)
Daughter, Thomasin, baptised 13 December 1615 and buried 10 June 1616, St Martin, Coney Street (PReg)
One of the petitioners for the incorporation of the London company of clockmakers 1630 (Loombes/66)
Cooke, Thomas
Son of a shoemaker, born at Allerthorpe [8 March] 1807. Came to York c. 1829 and, during part of the time taught mathematics and writing at the

Rev. John Shackleton's school in Micklegate (Taylor/41)

Married Hannah Milner of Skirpenbeck 10 September 1831 St Maurice (PReg)

Optician, 50 Stonegate (YG 4 March 1837) 12 Coney Street (YG 27 January 1849)

Purchased the site of the Duke's Hall on Bishophill where he built Buckingham Works, 1855 (Taylor/43)

Moved his shop to 26 Coney Street, once the premises of James Barber (q.v.), where he added clock and watchmaking to his business (YG 5 May 1860)

Died 19 October 1868 aged 61 at the Buckingham Works buried York Cemetery grave 795 disease of the nerves (YCReg and YG 24 October 1868)

His widow, Hannah, died 21 September 1884 aged 72 at St George's Place buried York Cemetery grave 795 (YCReg and YG 25 September 1884)

Cosens, Nicholas (Cussans)

Hourglass maker, Free 1639 (SS102/92)

Admitted to the freedom on payment of £6 13s 4d but if he married Mr Wade's daughter to have £3 6s 8d refunded to him, 15 January 1638 (YCA B36/17)

Married, first, 1639 Elizabeth Wade, she died 1652

Married, second, 1653, Jane Barnard. He died 1654 (Loomes/67)

Coster, Charles de

see Clarke, Charles

Coulton, Francis

Clockmaker, son of John Coulton (q.v.), clockmaker, Free by patrimony 1757 (SS102/278)

Coulton, John (Colton)

Clockmaker, son of Francis Coulton, baker, Free by patrimony (no trade given) 1702 (SS102/184)

Father of William Coulton, Free by patrimony 1740 (SS102/251)

Father of Francis Coulton, clockmaker, Free by patrimony 1757 (SS102/278)

Coulton, William

Watchmaker at Sign of the Dial, Stonegate (Loomes/66)

Death of son, William, 12 September, buried 14 September 1775 churchyard St Olaves (PReg)

Clockmaker of Stonegate 1758, 1784 (Poll) 1787 (Dir 1787)

Died March 1792 (YH 10 March 1792)

Cowlman, John

Son of Richard Cowlman of York, apprenticed to James Barber (q.v.), George Cattle (q.v.) and William North (q.v.), jewellers, indenture 5 March 1825, 7 years (YCA D16/152)

Coyle, James

Son of Miles Coyle of York, musician, apprenticed to Peter Goulett, (q.v.) jeweller, indenture 1 December 1766, 7 years, consideration £21 (YCA D14/95)

Crawfurth, Richard
Goldsmith, Free 1545 (SS96/266)

Creaser, Isaiah (Creasor)
Born 28 February baptised 1 March 1789 Holy Trinity, Micklegate (PReg)
Silversmith, son of William Creaser, innholder, [son of Thomas Creaser, farmer of Stillingfleet], Free by patrimony [28 February] 1811 (Malden)
Silversmith of Toft Green 1818, 1820, 1830 (Poll)
Widower, married Frances Turnbull 20 December 1824 Holy Trinity, Micklegate (PReg)
Father of Thomas Creaser, gardener, Free by patrimony 24 January 1846 (Malden)
Father of William Creaser, gardener, Free by patrimony 15 June 1846 (Malden)

Creaser, Luke
Son of William Creaser of Toft Green, York, farmer (innholder 1809), and Sarah, his wife, apprenticed to John Hampston (q.v.), John Prince (q.v.) Robert Cattle (q.v.) and George Cattle (q.v.), jewellers, indenture 17 December 1800, 8 years (YCA D15/34)
Married Catherine, daughter of John Potter of Fossgate, whip maker, 20 November 1808 Holy Trinity, Micklegate (PReg)
Jeweller, Free 1809 (Malden)
Of Fossgate, goldsmith and jeweller, son, John, born 20, baptised 23 and died 31 August, buried 1 September 1809 churchyard St Crux (PReg)
Assay at York 1809 (YAJ49/119)

Creaser, Thomas (Creasor, Creassor, Cressey)
Born 19 baptised 24 August 1792 Holy Trinity, Micklegate, son of William Creaser, cowkeeper (farmer in 1815), son of Thomas Creaser of Stillingfleet (PReg)
Watchmaker, Free by patrimony 21 October 1815, entered in register under the name of Cressey although he signed as Creassor (YCA Freedom claim & Malden)
Watchmaker of Toft Green, 1818, 1820, 1830 (Poll)

Crossley, Jonas
Dealer in hardware (Dir 1787)
Jeweller, goldsmith and tea dealer (Dir 1802)
In partnership with William Etherington (q.v.) of St Ann's Square, Manchester (Dir 1804)
Assay at York 1805 (YAJ49/119)
Died 25 April 1807 (Gubbins/23)

Cruttenden, Thomas (Crittenden, Crittandin)
Apprenticed to Robert Seignoir of London, March 1667–68 and then to John Fromanteel of London to 1678, Free of London November 1677 (Loomes/69)
Clockmaker, Free 1680 (SS102/154)
Wife, Mary, buried 22 November 1683 St Martin, Coney Street (PReg)
Married, second, 1684 Elizabeth Martin (Loomes/69)
Buried 8 August 1698 St Martin, Coney Street (PReg)

Father of Sidney Cruttenden, butcher, Free by patrimony 1720 (SS102/215)

Cullender, Thomas

Clockmaker, took apprentice Robert Brogden (q.v.) (Free 1714), no indenture registered (Malden)

Cure, Robert

Goldsmith, Free 1500 (SS96/224)

Cussins, Regge

Co–founder of Cussins and Light Ltd, domestic radio and electrical retailers, lived at Newland Park Close, an acknowledged expert on lapidary and worker in silver (YEP 9 September 1979)

Maker's mark, JC & RC, for Cussins and Light trading as Reggilla Jewels, registered with Sheffield Assay Office 4 October 1965 (letter from librarian at Sheffield Assay Office)

Died 11 February 1979 aged 78 (YEP 13 February 1979)

Custance, Thomas (Constance)

Goldsmith, son of James Custance, baker, Free by patrimony 1494 (SS96/219)

House in Colliergate and land in Acomb (YWCWG)

Will 13 May 1527 proved 30 March 1528, to be buried in the church of the Augustine Friars near his father. Executor and legatee wife, Isabell, who was not to remarry without the agreement of her brother, William Harrington, and her son, Henry. Left six best silver spoons that were his father's (YASRS11/43, YWCWG)

Cybright, Symon

Goldsmith of York

Will 2 July proved 18 July 1398, to be buried in the churchyard of York Minster (YASRS38/18, YWCWG)

Dade, Geoffrey

Goldsmith of York, mentioned in an undated pre–1530 document (SRJ/1587)

Dalburgh, John

Goldsmith, Free 1434 (SS96/148)

Dale, Edward John

Son of John Dale of York, grocer, apprenticed to James Barber (q.v.) and William North (q.v.), silversmiths and jewellers, indenture 18 November 1839, 7 years (YCA D16/397)

Dale, Robert de

Goldsmith, Free 1375 (SS96/73)

Of St Helen, Stonegate, parish, paid 4d poll tax 1377 (YAJ43/138)

Dalton, Stephen

Apprenticed to Jonathan Storr (q.v.), watchmaker, indenture 17 December 1792, 7 years, consideration £31 10s, tax of 15s 9d paid 21 December 1792 (PRO)

Dam, John

Goldsmith, Free 1483 (SS96/206)

Danger, Peter

Goldfiner, Free 1574 (SS102/16)

Daniel, Thomas

Son of Mary Daniel of Kirkham, Lancashire, widow, apprenticed to Henry Hindley (q.v.) of York, clockmaker, indenture 1 May 1761, 7 years, consideration £20, tax of £1 paid 2 May 1769 (PRO and YCA D14/44)

Papist, apprentice living with Henry Hindley, aged 20, 6 years resident in St Michael le Belfrey, 1767 (Aveling/283)

Darbyshire, George

Baptised 4 July 1763 St Michael, Spurriergate (PReg)

Jeweller of Crane Court, Fleet Street London, son of Christopher Darbyshire, aledraper, formerly skinner, Free by patrimony [17 June] 1789 (Malden)

Married Theresa, daughter of Captain Ryves, a senior officer in 1st West Yorkshire Militia, December 1795 London (RHS)

Sheriff of York 1801/2 (RHS)

Died in London 11 April 1834 aged 70 (RHS)

Darbyshire, Matthew

Baptised 15 October 1749 St Michael, Spurriergate (PReg)

Apprenticed to Peter Goulett (q.v.), jeweller, indenture, 25 October 1764, 7 years (YCA D14/76)

Jeweller, son of Christopher Darbyshire, coal merchant, Free by patrimony [19 October] 1772 (Malden)

Silversmith of Hull 1784 (Poll)

Jeweller of Wakefield 1807 (Poll)

Died at Spring Hill, New York State, USA (YCh 10 October 1818)

Darcy, William

Son of Thomas Darcy of York, gentleman, apprenticed to William Seamer (q.v.), watchmaker, and Dorothy, his wife, indenture 8 June 1635, 7 years (YCA D12/74)

Darling, William

Born 29 September baptised 5 October 1806 St Michael le Belfrey son (2nd child) of William Darling of Grape Lane, cordwainer, and Elizabeth daughter of Thomas Hall (PReg)

Son of William Darling, shoemaker of 21 Coney Street, apprenticed to James Barber (q.v.) And William Whitwell (q.v.), jewellers, indenture 11 Sept 1820, 7 years (YCA D14/63)

Watchmaker, Free by patrimony 18 August 1829 (YCA Freedom claim)

Watchmaker of Coney Street 1830 (Poll)

Watchmaker and jeweller 42 Coney Street (Dir 1851)

Died 6 July 1888, retired watchmaker of Starbeck, aged 82, buried York Cemetery grave 12935 paralysis (YCReg)

Davies, Richard

Apprenticed to Peter Goulett (q.v.), jeweller, indenture 14 March 1770, 7 years, consideration £30 (PRO)

Dayvell, William

Goldsmith, Free 1364 (SS96/58)

Deanome, Robert (Denham)

Goldsmith, Free 1559 (SS102/1)

Goldsmith of London with John Skofeld, stationer of York, who both had married daughters of Alderman William Holme of York, deceased, claimed the rights to the toll of the Malt Market in Coney Street which had been granted to their late father in law. On surrendering their rights to the Lord Mayor he was paid £6 13s 4d plus 13s 4d for his charges from London and in York and Skofeld was paid 13s 4d. (YCA B24/72b)

Demayne, Anthony
Son of Francis Demayne of Bardenscales in the parish of Skipton, yeoman, apprenticed to William Clark (q.v.), clock and watchmaker etc., indenture 10 December 1761, 7 years, consideration £23 2s (YCA D14/50)

Dempster, Anthony
Apprenticed to Robert Lonsdale, carpenter and joiner, Free 1772 (Malden)
Joiner of the Liberty of Mint Yard 1800 (YCA Freedom claim)
Clock and watchmaker of Walmgate (Dir 1823)
Joiner of Mint Yard 1830 (Poll)

Dempster, [Mark] Anthony
Born 26 December 1800 in the Liberty of Mint Yard, son of Anthony Dempster, baptised Jubbergate Chapel (YCA Freedom claim)
Clock and watchmaker of the parish of St Peter the Little, son of Anthony Dempster, joiner, Free by patrimony 15 October 1829 (YCA Freedom claim)
Clock and watchmaker of 49 Jubbergate (Dir 1830)
Watchmaker of Feasegate 1830 (Poll)
Married Ann Kirk of Acomb 21 November 1833 St Olaves (PReg and YG 23 November 1833)
By 1834 had moved to Richmond. Died 24 December 1875 aged 75 Shedforth, County Durham (Loomes/71)

Dewe, John
Goldsmith, Free 1398 (SS96/99)
Fined 5s 0d for making false silver 1397/8 (SS102/248)

Dickinson
see Dycconson

Dickinson, Robert
Born 25 November baptised 28 December 1789 St Peter, Liverpool (YCA Freedom claim)
Watchmaker [of St Martin cum Gregory parish], son of Thomas Dickinson, joiner and cabinetmaker [of Church Street, Liverpool 1789], deceased, Free by patrimony 5 January 1811 (Malden)
Clock and watchmaker of Goodramgate (Dir 1823)

Dickson
see Dykson

Dinmore, Richard
Clock and watchmaker, succeeded Jonathan Storr (q.v.) in his business at Minster Gates. He had been foreman at John Hampston (q.v.), John Prince (q.v.), Robert Cattle (q.v.) and George Cattle (q.v.), jewellers and silversmiths (YkCo 15 July 1805)
Assigned his effects (YkCo 23 November 1807)

Watchmaker of Coppergate (Dir 1818)
Watch and clock maker and teadealer of Coppergate (Dir 1823)
Died in the Groves (YG 29 June 1833)

Dishforth, Thomas de
Goldsmith of York
Grantor of a messuage with buildings in Bootham 1258x1296 (SRJ/612)

Dixon, Thomas
Goldsmith
Inquest at the Lammas Assizes concerning his theft of a pyx from St Michael, Spurriergate, January 1547–January 1548 (StMSp 3/87b)

Dorem, Richard de
Goldsmith, Free 1317 (SS96/17)

Dorem, Simon de (Durem)
Goldsmith of York
Witness to a grant of land in Walmgate 13 June 1304 (BTC16/106)
Witness to a grant of land in Fossgate 1305 (BTC16/59)
Witness to a grant of land in Fossgate 1316 (BTC16/60)
Legatee of the will, 28 April 1328, of Nicholas Gaudyn (q.v.), goldsmith (YWCWG)

Doughty, John
Clock and watchmaker of St Michael le Belfrey parish
Married Ann Guisley of Holy Trinity, Goodramgate, parish 9 February 1772 St Michael le Belfrey (PReg)

Dowbyggins, Martin
Dubyggin, Martin
see Byggyn, Martin du

Duce, John
Son of John Duce of York, shoemaker, apprenticed to John Hampston (q.v.), John Prince (q.v.), Robert Cattle (q.v.) and George Cattle (q.v.), jewellers and silversmiths, indenture 25 April 1803, 7 years (YCA D15/168)

Ducheman, Kenrick
Goldsmith, died 1571 (Jackson/298)

Duke, William
Goldsmith, Free 1417 (SS96/124)
Will 21 May 1440 proved 2 June 1440, to be buried at St Michael le Belfrey. Executor and legatee wife, Isota. Witness to and legatee of will, John Newland (q.v.), goldsmith (YASRS38/21, YWCWG)

Durrem, John de
Goldsmith, son of John de Durem, wright, Free by patrimony 1414 (SS96/121)

Durham
see Dorem, Durrem

Dutton William
Working jeweller and watchmaker, 6½ Coney Street (Dir 1867)

Dycconson, John
Goldsmith, Free 1589 (SS102/32)

Dyke, John
Goldsmith, Free 1427 (SS96/139)
Dykson, Robert
Goldsmith, Free 1470 (SS96/190)
Eandinnus
Goldsmith of York, paid rental of 7d, 1301 (YASRS21/121)
Ede, Richard de
Goldsmith, Free 1377 (SS96/75)
Edwards, Thomas
Silversmith of Holy Trinity, Goodramgate, parish married Mary Morrod, widow, 6 January 1798 at St Crux (PReg)
Of Petergate (YkCo 5 August 1805)
Edwards, William
Goldsmith, father of Edmund Edwards basket–maker (Free 1679) (SS102/151)
Ellis, James
Watchmaker, son of Brian Ellis, parchment–maker, Free by patrimony 1637 (SS102/89)
Ellis, John (Elys, Ellysse)
Goldsmith, Free 1416 (SS96/124)
Will 25 August 1429 proved 30 August 1429, to be buried at St John, Ousebridge. Executor and legatee wife, Agnes. Witness Walter Spendeluf (q.v.), goldsmith (YASRS6/58, YWCWG)
Ellis, John
Goldsmith, son of Thomas Ellis, merchant tailor, Free by patrimony 1758 (SS102/283)
Goldsmith of Coney Street 1758 (Poll)
Ellison, Robert
Son of Robert Ellison of York, innkeeper, apprenticed to Robert Cattle (q.v.) and James Barber (q.v.), jewellers and silversmiths, indenture 3 June 1809, 7 years (YCA D15/234)
Jeweller of Holy Trinity, King's court, parish married there Ann Lupton of St Olaves parish 24 December 1819 (PReg)
Silversmith, Free 1820 (Malden)
Working jeweller, 5 Brunswick Place (Dir 1830)
Dead by January 1870 when his youngest daughter, Emma, died (YG 29 January 1870)
Elsey, William
Goldsmith, Free 1675 (SS102/145)
Elston, Thomas
Son of Ellen Elston, widow, apprenticed to Richard Clark (q.v.), jeweller and goldsmith, indenture 7 February 1781, 7 years, consideration £10 (YCA D14/217)
Elton, William
Watchmaker, 5 St Sampson's Square (Dir 1846)
Of Clarence Street, died 21 January 1847 aged 64 buried York Cemetery public grave 15143 natural decay (YCReg)

Emondson, Lawrence (Edmonson)

Goldsmith, son of Christopher Emondson, cordwainer, Free by patrimony 1535 (SS96/254)

Employed to weigh chalices and other jewels at St Michael, Spurriergate, January 1537–January 1538 (StMSp 4/143b)

Bought four ounces of broken plate, stolen by Thomas Bennett, late footman to the Duchess of Richmond, after the Lord Mayor had made a proclamation concerning it. The stolen plate was delivered to two of the chamberlains, 15 November 1541 (YCA B15/60b)

Of Ousebridge, will 11 March 1542 proved 10 May 1543 to be buried St Michael, Spurriergate. Executor and legatee wife Jennet, daughter of William Mowbray (YASRS11/57, YWCWG)

Father of Martin Emondson, tyler, Free by patrimony 1556 (SS96/277)

Emondson, Ralph (Emson, Emerson)

Goldsmith, son of John Emondson, attorney of Ouse Bridge, Free by patrimony 1559 (SS102/2)

Fined 1s 8d by the two wardens of the London company during their searches in the north and paid 3s 4d for his oath of good workmanship, 5 February 1561 (LGC minute book K/176)

Swore an oath of good workmanship and paid 1s to the London company during their searches in the north. Also paid 3s for the swearing of an oath by his servant John Bewe (q.v.), 17 July 1573 (LGC minute book L/158–9)

Leased feoffment of a tenement, formerly called the Paycocke, now called the Maiden Head in Fossgate in St Crux parish, in the occupation of Ralph Emondson and his wife Joan, to John Fell of York, cook, 25 January 1583 (SS186/292)

Sale of above tenement etc., to John Fell, £80, 30 January 1583 (SS186/293)

Epworth, Elizabeth

Jeweller etc., 79 Low Petergate (Dir 1876)

Jeweller and silversmith, 22 Spurriergate, established 1831 [This date relates to the firm of pawn–brokers founded by her father, Charles Epworth, in Precentors' Court and sold by his wife, Rachel, to Henry Hardcastle of Lady Peckett's Yard in 1871 (YG 23 September 1879)] (YG 5 January 1878)

Silversmith, jeweller and electro–plater, 16 Spurriergate (Dir 1879)

Watchmaker, gold and silversmith, 14 Spurriergate (1895)

Disposed of her business to William Grant (q.v.) (YG 8 April 1905)

Of 206 Kings road, Harrogate, died 1 February 1919 aged 71 buried York Cemetery grave 2194 cancer (YCReg)

Erbery, Thomas

Goldsmith, Free 1445, who owes — (SS96/163)

Erkenden, Henry de

Goldbeater, Free 1317 (SS96/17)

Erkendene, John de

Goldbeater, Free 1300 (SS96/8)

Holder of land between Glovergail and Patrickpool 3 June 1346 (YASRS148/309)

Eschaunge, John del

see Chaunge

Eston, John

Goldsmith, Free 1445 (SS96/163)

Esyngwald, Henry

Goldsmith of York

Will 25 April 1402 proved 11 August 1403 to be buried in the churchyard of St Michael le Belfrey. Residuary legatee wife, Agnes(YASRS38/22, YWCWG)

Etherington, Isaac

Apprenticed to his father, William Etherington (q.v.), goldsmith etc., indenture 24 May 1793, 7 years, consideration £21 (PRO)

Etherington, Thomas

Watchmaker, Free 1686 (SS102/161)

Chamberlain 1708 (SS102/193)

Fined £70 for refusing to take office of Sheriff, 22 September 1718 (YCA B41/192)

Quaker, died 8 April 1728 (Loomes/76)

Father of Rebecca Etherington, spinster, Free by patrimony 1728 (SS102/229)

Father of Thomas Etherington (q.v.), watchmaker, Free by patrimony 1741 (SS102/257)

Etherington, Thomas

Watchmaker, son of Thomas Etherington (q.v.), watchmaker, Free by patrimony 1741 (SS102/257)

Etherington, William *

Jeweller, gold and silversmith, opened a shop in St Helen's Square (YkCo 1 August 1786)

Jeweller (Dir 1787)

Bought of W. Etherington Working Jeweller, Gold & Silversmith, St. Helen's Square.

Silversmith and jeweller of St Helen's Square, son of Ambrose Etherington, merchant tailor, Free by patrimony 1788

Commissioned to prepare a gold box for the Freedom of the Duke of Cumberland 20 July 1789 (YCA B45/351). Bill for £62 9s 6d (£52 10s for box and £9 19s 6d for three sets of silver knives and forks) presented 30 August 1789, authorised for payment 19 January 1790 (YCA C70)

Supplied the Corporation with 3 sets of knives and forks for £11 0s 6d, 1795 and an inscribed silver salver for £25, 1797 (Gubbins/23)

Married Miss E. Marshall, daughter of James Marshall (YH 4 June 1791)

Of William Etherington and Jonas Crossley (q.v.), working jewellers of St Ann's Square, Manchester (Dir 1804)

Assay at York 1805 (YAJ49/119)

Farrer, Samuel

Son of Roger Farrer, baptised 22 September 1625 St Michael le Belfrey (PReg)

Watchmaker, son of Roger Farrer, tailor, Free by patrimony 1649 (SS102/107)

Fattorini, Joseph

Married Jusepa Cattaneo 30 January 1837 St Mary, Castlegate (PReg)

Jeweller in partnership with Henry Cattaneo (q.v.) and Phillip Cattaneo (q.v.) in Castlegate as Cattaneo & Co. formerly of King's Staithe carrying on the same business in partnership with Henry Cattaneo, Phillip Cattaneo, Austin Cattaneo (q.v.), John Cattaneo (q.v.) and Peter Ballorini (q.v.) as Cattaneo & Co (YG 7 October 1848)

Perhaps a member of the same family as Fattorini and Sons which was founded by Antonio Fattorini, born near Lake Como, Italy. He established a business in Leeds in 1797 and moved to Harrogate 1831 (Hulme 1/153)

Of 30 Parliament Street, watchmaker (Dir 1846, 1849)

Of 18 Stonegate, jeweller (Dir 1851, 1855)

Wife, Elizabeth, of Laurence Street died 22 August 1875 buried York Cemetery grave 14598 phthisis (YCReg)

Of St Sampson's Square, jeweller, died 18 October 1875 aged 73 buried York Cemetery grave 14598 (YCReg)

Feled, John

Goldsmith, Free 1443 (SS96/161)

Femyndyn, Bernard

Goldsmith, Free 1414 (SS96/120)

Fennay, Michael

Goldsmith, Free 1503 (SS96/227)

Fenton, James

Clockmaker, son of Thomas Fenton, brickmaker, Free by Patrimony 1741 (SS102/260)

Clockmaker of Long Lane, London, 1741 (Poll)

Ferrand, William

Son of William Ferrand of York, plane–maker, apprenticed to John Hampston (q.v.), John Prince (q.v.), Robert Cattle (q.v.) and George Cattle (q.v.), jewellers and silversmiths, indenture 18 April 1800, 8 years (YCA D15/139)

Forester, Henry (Forster)

Goldsmith, Free 1401 (SS96/104)

Searcher 1417/8 (SS120/247) 3 November 1420 (SS186/58)

Occupant of a tenement in Stonegate, once in possession John Clyveland (q.v.), goldsmith, rent paid £4, 11 March 1421 (SS120/75)

Forester, Thomas
Goldsmith, Free 1397 (SS96/98)
Witness to the will, 5 September 1433, of William Gateshede (q.v.), goldsmith (YWCWG)

Forth, John del
Goldsmith, Free 1363 (SS96/57)

Foss, Thomas
Of Pontefract, apprenticed to Joseph Hindley (q.v.), clock and watchmaker, indenture 1 October 1765, 8 years from 1 May 1865, consideration £8 (YCA D14/84)

Foster, Jesper
Goldsmith, Free 1617 (SS102/66)

Foster, Robert
Goldsmith, died in 1719 (Jackson/299)

Foster, William *1570–72
Goldsmith, Free 1569 (SS102/11)
Married Margaret Londer 9 July 1570 St Michael le Belfrey. Their children baptised there 1575–1584 (PReg)
Elected searcher 15 January 1583 (YCA B28/121)
Of St Michael le Belfrey, with wife, appeared before the Archiepiscopal Visitation and swore they both communicated (Aveling/206)
Died 1610 (Jackson/298)

Foughbrigg, John
Goldbeater, Free 1390 (SS96/89)

Fox, William
Goldsmith of Tyverington [Terrington], Free 1356 (SS96/50)
Probably nephew of William Fox of Cornborough, MP for York 1328, 1330, 1332 Chamberlain 1338 (SS/96/32) Bailiff 1342/3 (RHS)
Matilda, wife of William Fox, goldsmith, left 20s in will, 7 January 1360, of John Freboys of York (SS186/147)
Paid rent, with Thomas de Blackburn (q.v.), goldsmith, for a tenement opposite the Cross on Ouse bridge, 36s, 25 January 1376 (SS120/6)
Elected, with William le Crull, to be responsible for the repair of the staithe between Ouse bridge and the Friars Minor 9 February 1376 (SS120/19)
Owner of tenements in Thurs Lane [Middle Water Lane] and a garden and land in Fishergate (YWCWG)
Will 26 April 1393 proved 4 June 1393 to be buried in St Mary, Castlegate. Executor and legatee wife Matilda. Left 12 silver spoons with decorated knobs (YASRS6/65, YWCWG)
Will of widow, Matilda, 15 April 1407 proved 2 November 1407 (YASRS6/65)

Fox, Thomas
Watchmaker without Castlegate Postern, died 23 buried 25 November 1802 aged 54 buried in the churchyard, St Mary, Castlegate, dropsy (PReg)

Fox, William
Jeweller, 9 St Helen's Square (Dir 1830)
Francis, B
Watch repairer (YkCo 24 August 1784)
House in High Ousegate for sale or let (YkCo 18 August 1785)
Francis, Thomas (Frauncez)
Goldsmith, son of Robert Francis, tapiter, Free by patrimony 1503 (SS96/227)
Franco
Goldsmith, sold land in Bootham – late 12th century (EYC1/214)
Fraunceys, John
Jeweller, Free 1445 (SS96/163)
Freman, Edward
Goldsmith, Free 1592 (SS102/34)
Known in 1638 (Jackson/298)
Freideberg, Solomon
Jeweller, 59 Goodramgate (Dir 1851)
Frese, Henry
Goldsmith, Free 1399 (SS96/102)
Father of William Frese (q.v.) goldsmith, Free by patrimony 1431 (SS96/144)
Frese, William
Goldsmith, son of Henry Frese (q.v.) (Free 1399), Free by patrimony 1431 (SS96/144)
Frost, John
Goldsmith, son of William Frost (q.v.) (Free 1595), Free by patrimony 1623 (SS102/73)
Frost, William
Goldsmith, Free 1595 (SS102/38)
Father of John Frost (q.v.), goldsmith, Free by patrimony 1623 (SS102/73)
Died in 1618 (Jackson/298)
Fryer, Grace
Daughter of late William Buttle of York, married William Fryer, clock and watchmaker (YCh 23 October 1817)
Continued her husbands business after his death (YG 13 April 1822)
Clock and watchmaker, High Ousegate (Dir 1823)
Fryer, John
Born 2 baptised 4 July 1785 Holy Trinity, King's Court (PReg)
Watchmaker of Pocklington, [first] son of William Fryer [son of John Fryer of Norton], victualler, Free by patrimony [17 October] 1812 (Malden)
Premises at Waterloo Buildings, Pocklington, 1823 until his death in 1830. Succeeded by his wife, Maria, 1830–1843 (Walker/70)
Fryer, Michael Edwin
Son of John Fryer of York, apprenticed to Andrew Kleiser (q.v.) and Joseph Kleiser (q.v.), clock and watchmakers, indenture 4 November 1852, 7 years, no consideration (YCA D494)

Fryer, William
>Baptised 4 February 1787 Holy Trinity, King's Court (PReg)
>Watchmaker of Hull, son of William Fryer, victualler, deceased, Free by patrimony [5 December] 1809 (Malden)
>Of Pocklington 1810 (Dinsdale/55) Probably living at Canal Inn but working in York (Walker/70)
>Married Grace, eldest daughter of the late William Buttle of York (YCh 23 October 1817)
>Watchmaker of Pavement (Dir 1818)
>Recommenced business in High Ousegate, York (YG 10 June 1820)
>Owing to ill health his stock to be sold and the house and shop, a very desirable situation for a watchmaker, to be let (YH 18 August 1821)
>House occupied by him in High Ousegate to be let (YG 13 October 1821)
>Death at Pocklington aged 34 (YG 9 February 1822)
>Widow, Grace Fryer (q.v.), continued business (YG 13 April 1822)

Gainsford, Robert
>Plater, close plater and silversmith of Eyre Street, Sheffield. Formerly in partnership with Alexander Goodman (q.v.) as Goodman, Gainsford & Co. Maker's mark registered at Sheffield 1808. Assays at York 27 May 1809. Robert Gainsford & Co. manufacturers of silver and plated goods 1815 (YAJ49/120)

Gale, George (Gaile, Gayll, Gayle)
>Goldsmith, Free 1514 (SS96/236)
>Son of Oliver Gale of Thirntoft, Yorkshire, married, Mary, daughter of Robert Lord of Kendal in the parish of Driffield (Foster)
>Member of Corpus Christi Guild 1511 (SS57/174)
>Paid 8s for gilding the city's great mace 1523/4 (Jewitt/456)
>Alderman 1525 (RHS)
>Master of Royal Mint at York c.1528 (Palliser/108)
>Sheriff 29 September 1530 (RHS)
>MP for York 13 January 1532 and 15 December 1541 (B11/135, B15/63b, Park/49)
>Lord Mayor 1534, 1549 (SS96/253 & 268)
>Supervisor of the will, 13 June 1538, of Richard Pygot (q.v.), goldfiner (YWCWG)
>Under–treasurer of Royal Mint when it reopened in 1545 (Palliser/108)
>Granted, with wife, site of Wilberfoss Priory and lands in Newton for a payment of £615 18s 1d, 8 April 1553 (YASRS48/167)
>Owner of a garden in Little St Andrewgate, three cottages with garths and closes in Peasholme, a close with Pound Garth in Peasholme, 14 closes, lands and tenements at Hundeburton, certain lands in Escrick called the Greyfriars land, all tenements and land in Catton, and the Manor lands and tenements in Escrick (YWCWG)
>Died 12 July 1556 buried York Minster, MI in south transept (Drake/497)
>Will 11 June 1556 proved 27 August 1556, to be buried in Holy Trinity, Goodramgate, in the closet nigh his stall. Executor and legatee wife, Mary (YWCWG)

Will of widow, of Holy Trinity, Goodramgate, 24 September 1557 proved 18 March 1557, she desired to be buried in York Minster (RHS)

Gatcliffe, Francis

Jeweller, Free by order 1756 (SS102/277)

Jeweller of Girdlergate [Church Street] 1758, 1784 (Poll)

Gatcliffe, Samuel

Goldsmith of St Sampson's parish, daughter Kitty, 9th child, born in the city poorhouse, baptised 24 September 1783 St Olave's (PReg)

Gatesheved, William de (Gateshede)

Goldsmith, Free 1396 (SS96/97)

Chamberlain 1412 (SS96/115)

Owner of a tenement in North Street 28 July 1421 (SS186/47)

Sheriff 1423/4 (Drake/362)

Will 5 September 1433 proved 2 October 1433, to be buried in the choir in his parish church, St Edward in the suburbs without Walmgate Bar. Executor and legatee wife, Margaret. Witness Thomas Forest[er] (q.v.), goldsmith (YASRS6/68, YWCWG)

Widow, Margaret, will 17 Sept 1442 pro 15 January 1442, to be buried in All Saints, North Street. Left silver box, three knives with silver gilt handles, six silver spoons with 'fretletters', two antique silver spoons, a maple goblet decorated with silver, four gold rings and a gold necklace YASRS6/68, YWCWG)

Gaudin

Goldsmith

Witness to a quitclaim, 4 April 1282 (YASRS50/204)

Holder of two tofts in Bootham, paid rent (husgabel) of 2d on them, 1284 (YAJ50/86)

Land in the parish of St Edward in the suburbs, Walmgate, ceded to him by Robert le Grant (q.v.), goldsmith, 20 July 1282 (BTC16/110) by Elwisa, widow of William Saper, 17 June 1284 (BTC16/110), by Ellen, daughter of Robert le Grant, 13 May 1285, (BTC16/111) and by Eudo of Touthorpe, 8 March 1292 and 10 July 1294 (BTC16/111 and 112)

Receipt by Margaret, daughter of Ralph de Buthum to Gaudin for £5 of silver, part payment of money left to her by her father, 19 November 1285 (YASRS50/204)

Wife, Mariota, and daughter, Ellen, wife of Ralph de Buthum mentioned in a quitclaim concerning receipts from land in Walmgate, 11 May 1290 (BTC16/105)

Land in the parish of St Edward in the suburbs, Walmgate granted to his son, Gaudin, 19 July 1293 (BTC16/112)

Grant of land in St Laurence parish from Thomas, son of Paulinus de Eltoft, !0 April 1294 (BTC16/118)

Withdrawal of a plea of trespass made by German (q.v.), the goldsmith against Gaudin and his sons, Nicholas and John, 5 July 1303 (BTC16/106)

Daughter, Ibota, mentioned in a quitclaim concerning land in the parish of St Edward in the suburbs, Walmgate, 7 September 1303 (BTC16/114)

Grant from his son, Nicholas Gaudyn (q.v.), goldsmith, of rents from land in the parish of St Edward in the suburbs, Walmgate, 25 April 1311 (BTC16/115)

Son, John, mentioned in a quitclaim concerning property of the Merchant Adventurers' Company in Monkgate, 1313 (BTC16/98)

Son, Nicholas [Gaudin] (q.v.), Free by patrimony 1315 (SS96/16)

Son, Thomas, made a grant of land in Walmgate to his sister, Mariota, 30 July 1316 (BTC16/116)

Deceased by 13 November 1328 (BTC16/117)

Daughters, Isabel, wife of Richard de Tickhill, merchant of York, and Mariota, wife of William atte Water, merchant of York mentioned in a quitclaim concerning property of the Merchant Adventurers' Company in Monkgate, 1335 (BTC16/98)

Gaudyn, Nicholas

Withdrawal of a plea of trespass made by German (q.v.), the goldsmith against Gaudin (q.v.) and his sons, Nicholas and John, 5 July 1303 (BTC16/106)

Goldsmith, grant to his father of rents from land in the parish of St Edward in the suburbs, Walmgate, 25 April 1311 (BTC16/115)

Son of Gaudin, goldsmith, Free by patrimony 1314 (SS96/16)

Paid poll tax of 4s 4¼d on property in St Crux parish valued at £4 7s, 1327 (YASRS74/162)

Owner of property in Skeldergate and Colliergate (YWCWG)

Will 28 April 1328, to be buried in St Edward in the suburbs, Walmgate. Left 18 silver spoons. Legatee Simon de Dorem (q.v.), goldsmith (BTC16/117, YWCWG)

Grant by his executors of land in Walmgate, 2 July 1328 (BTC16/117)

Geldart, John

Watchmaker, son of Joshua Geldart (q.v.), goldsmith, Free by patrimony 1675 (SS102/144)

Geldart, Joshua *1650

Goldsmith, Free 1646 (SS102/102)

Wife, Ann, buried 12 February 1660 St Martin, Coney Street (PReg)

Buried 4 September 1663 St Martin, Coney Street, in the middle aisle (PReg)

Will 11 August 1663 (YASRS49/35)

Father of John Geldart (q.v.), watchmaker, Free by patrimony 1675 (SS102/144)

Gell, John

Watchmaker, son of Edward Gell, locksmith, Free by patrimony 1635 (SS102/86)

Married Jane Pawson of Leeds 1635 (Loomes/87)

Wife, Jane, buried 14 June 1636 St Martin, Coney Street (PReg)

Married 1636 Susan Mangie, widow (Loomes/87)

Father of John Gell, watchmaker, Free by patrimony 1663 (SS102/129)

Gell, John

Baptised 30 March 1636 St Martin, Coney Street (PReg)

Watchmaker, son of John Gell (q.v.), watchmaker, Free by patrimony 1663

(SS102/129)
Died 1698 (Loomes/87)

Genyn

See Jonyn

Geoffrey (Galfrido)

Goldsmith, quitclaim by Robert, son of Hugh the tiler, Gregory of Ripon, Robert the Clerk and Paulin the tailor and their respective wives, Agnes, Bella, Alice and Hawise, daughters and heirs of Geoffrey, the goldsmith, of land in St Andrewgate which John Stoyl had once held of Geoffrey and his wife Hawise, 1220x1224 (YASRS148/253)

German

The goldsmith

Witness to documents 1282 (SRJ/3209 and 3211–18)

Quitclaim to him by Paulinus, son of Paulinus (q.v.), the goldsmith, of land in Fossgate 1299 (BTC16/58)

Owner of land near Swinegate 20 October 1302 (YASRS148/271)

Withdrawal of a plea against Gaudin (q.v.) the goldsmith and his sons, Nicholas and John 5 July 1303 (BTC16/106)

Owner of land in Skeldergate, 11 May 1311 (YASRS39/216)

Grant by John, his son, of land and buildings in Fossgate 1316 (BTC16/60)

Gerveys, William

Goldbeater, Free 1396 (SS96/97)

Gibson, George *1679–82

Goldsmith, Free 1679 (SS102/150)

Known in 1684 (Jackson/299)

Giles, William

Son of John Giles of Clifton, apprenticed to James Barber (q.v.) and William Whitwell (q.v.), jewellers, indenture 18 September 1820, 7 years (YCA D16/63)

Jeweller of Earnest Street, Regent's Park, London, Free 1830 (Poll & Malden)

Gill, Mark *1677–90

Goldsmith, son of George Gill, glover, Free by patrimony 1681 (SS102/155)

Married Katherine Day 10 February 1683 St Michael le Belfrey. She was buried there 20 August 1687 (PReg)

Chamberlain 1687 (SS102/162)

Married second Mary. She was buried at St Michael le Belfrey 9 January 1694 (PReg)

Sheriff 1692/3 (Drake/367)

Alderman 11 September 1695 (RHS)

Lord Mayor 1697 (SS102/176)

Appeared before John Cooper of the London company for selling gold and silver wares worse than the standard. Ordered to pay £3 4s 6d, the cost of the goods, with charges of £6 11s, 27 May 1700 (LGC Court Book 10/216)

On paying £6 15s 6d towards the above order discharged from the remainder, 23 August 1700 (LGC Court Book 10/220)

Buried 12 Feb 1704 St Michael le Belfrey (PReg)

Will proved 17 February 1704 administration granted to his son Thomas (RHS)

Gill, Thomas

Goldsmith, late of York, declared a bankrupt and was required to surrender himself to the Commissioners on 3, 10 and 27 November 1721, at the first of which sittings the creditors were to come to prove their debts, pay contribution money and choose assignees (LG6000 24/28 October 1721)

Gilliot, Sir John (Gyllyot, Gylliot)

Merchant [and goldsmith], [eldest] son of John Gylliot, merchant [Lord Mayor 1464 and 1474, and his wife, Joan], Free by patrimony 1481 (SS96/203)

Admitted, with wife, Katherine, as member of Mercers' Guild 1480 (Cartulary/5b)

Member, with wife, Katherine [dead by 1488], of Corpus Christi Guild (SS57/109)

Chamberlain 1482 (SS96/203)

Sheriff 1484/5 (Drake/363)

Master of Merchant Adventurers' Company 1485/6, 1500/1 (SS129/322 and 323)

Alderman 22 May 1487 (RHS)

MP for York 16 October 1487 (YCA B6/112)

Second wife, Maude, daughter of Sir Henry Vavasour of Haslewood, admitted to Corpus Christi Guild 1489, she died before 28 December 1509 (SS57/126)

Lord Mayor 1490 and 1503 (SS96/214, 227)

Knight of the Bath 1500/1 (RHS)

Owner of lands and tenements in parishes of All Saints, Pavement, St Mary, Castlegate, in Coney Street in parish of St Martin, in Stonegate in parish of St Helen, in Fossgate, a great house in Coppergate, in Middle Water Lane, a tenement in Monkgate in parish of St Maurice, two tenements in Fishergate, two tenements in parish of Holy Trinity, King's Court, garths in the parish of St John, Hungate, and five tenements in Stonebow Lane (YWCWG)

Died 22 February 1509 (RHS)

Will 28 December proved 4 March 1509 to be buried with the body of Dame Maude, his [second] wife, in a chapel to be built in the church of St Saviour. Left five gilt standing pieces and a gold chain (YWCWG)

Inquest *post mortem* 2 October 1510, seized of lands in Bishopthorpe, Fulford, Towthorpe, Meltonby, Yapham and Kelfield (RHS)

Gillyan, John

Goldsmith, Free 1458 (SS96/177)

Godson, George

Goldsmith, known in 1583 (Jackson/298)

Godyer, George

Son of Thomas Godyer of York, pewterer, Free by patrimony as a draper

1556 (SS96/276)
Goldsmith when his son Edward Godyer, linen–draper, became Free by patrimony in 1583 (SS102/25)

Goldbeater, Bartholomew (alias Seman)
Goldsmith and citizen of London, master and warden of the King's monies of gold and silver in the Tower of London and the town of Calais, authorized to coin at York and Bristol 16 February 1423 (Cooper/152)
Appointed master and worker of the mistery of the King's Mint within his castle at York 16 Jan 1424 (CRP 2 Henry VI part 1/169)
Sent to York to coin there the gold and silver of the said country that was not the right weight and to remain there during the King's pleasure.(Cooper/152 & 153) Died 1432 (Reddaway/305)

Goldbeater, Henry le
Chamberlain 1332 (SS96/26)
Bailiff 1332/3 (Drake/360)
Of All Saints, North Street, parish, paid poll tax of 12d on property valued at 20s 1327 (YASRS74/168)
Of All Saints, North Street, parish, paid 8s poll tax 1334 (YkHist13/12)
Elected MP for York 23 September 1336, 1337, 1340 and 1341 (RHS, Park/43)
Mayor 3 February 1345 (SS96/38)
Witness to a grant 3 June 1346 (YASRS148/310)
Witness to a grant 15 July 1346 (BTC16/118)

Goldbeater, John le
Witness to a grant, 25 April 1303 (BLI12/16)
Chamberlain 1314 (SS96/15)
Bailiff 1319/20 (YCA D1/290)
Recipient of a messuage in Micklegate 1331 (SRJ/120)
Of St Martin cum Gregory parish, paid 4s poll tax 1334 (YkHist13/13)
Witness to documents 1337 (SRJ/1782 and 1783)

Goldsbrough, Charles *1701
Goldsmith, son of John Goldsbrough, vintner, Free by patrimony 1682 (SS102/156)

Goldsmith, Herman
[Goldsmith], Free 1464 (SS96/185)
Paid 2s 6d 'pro defectu in arte sua' 1468 (SS192/121)
Concerned in a slander in which Thomas Welles (q.v.) had called him an 'untrew man' and a 'false theiff' 14 November 1476 (YCA B1/13b)
Paid 11s for the gilt setting for the new sheath made for the mayor's great sword 1478 (SS192/165)
Bound himself for £10 to accept arbitration in a dispute with John Smyth, barber, 1487 (Attreed/602)
For repairing 6 silver thuribles and doing work on the shrine of St William and the reliquary of St Peter in York Minster, 10s 3d, 1497/8 (SS35/90)
For various repairs in York Minster on the shrine of St William, mending thuribles, boxes, a crozier, a water sprinkler and the vestments of the boy bishop using silver and gold, 17s 11d, 1498/9 (SS35/92)

For mending some jewels in York Minster, 8s 5d, 1504 (SS35/93)

Father of William Goldsmith (q.v.), Free by patrimony 1514 (SS96/236)

Goldsmith, Robert le

Witness to a grant 6 October 1343 (YASRS148/199)

Goldsmith, William

Goldsmith, Free 1459 (SS96/178)

Witness in slander action concerning Thomas Welles (q.v.) and Herman Goldsmith (q.v.) 14 November 1476 (YCA B1/13b)

Goldsmith, William

Son of Herman Goldsmith (q.v.), goldsmith (Free 1464), Free by patrimony 1514 (SS96/236)

Employed by church wardens of St Michael, Spurriergate, to 'piece and set together an old cross, and for burnishing it and for lattern it', January 1546–January 1547 (StMSp 3/79 & 4/213b)

'For taking in sunder of the silver cross head and weighing of other plate. For a pyx of copper and mending it, January 1547–January 1548 (StMSp 3/85)

Goodman, Alexander

Manufacturer of silver and plated articles, in partnership with Robert Gainsford (q.v.) and George Fairburn as Goodman, Gainsford & Co of Hawley Croft, Sheffield. Maker's marks registered at Sheffield 1800 and 1801. Assay at York 11 August 1807. Partnership dissolved c.1808 (YAJ49/120)

Gorras, John (Garyas, Goras)

Goldsmith, son of Walter Gorras (q.v.), goldsmith (Free 1441), Free by patrimony 1465 (SS96/185)

Searcher, witness in slander action concerning Thomas Welles (q.v.) and Herman Goldsmith (q.v.) 14 November 1476 (YCA B1/13b)

For repairing the head of St William, the image of St Appolonia, some thuribles, books of gospels and beakers in York Minster, 6s 6d, 1478/9 (SS35/84)

For repairing a gold chalice, a silver box, some thuribles, a gold cross and doing work on the shrine of St William in York Minster, 20s, 1481/2 (SS35/86)

For repairing a silver phial, some chalices and thuribles, the clasp and knobs of a missal and doing work on the shrine of St William in York Minster, 8s, 1485 (SS35/89)

Gorras, Walter

Goldsmith, father of John Gorras (q.v.), goldsmith (Free 1465), Free by patrimony 1441 (SS96/158)

Goulett, Peter

Jeweller, Free by order 1756 (SS102/277)

Son of Mr Goulett, jeweller, who kept the Great Pearl necklace shop in Leicester Fields, London (RHS)

Jeweller from London, starts business at the Golden Crown, Petergate (YkCo 20 January 1756)

Removed to Golden Crown, Stonegate, next door to Hillyard's bookshop

(YkCo 6 July 1756)

Jeweller of Blake Street 1758 (Poll)

Removes from a shop opposite the Assembly Rooms in Blake Street to the house next door to Miss Reynoldson's in the same street (YkCo 7 December 1762)

Jeweller and toyman in Blake Street, opens a shop in Long Room Street, Scarborough (YkCo 10 July 1764)

Chamberlain 3 February 1767 (YCA B44/218)

Married Grace Stead, widow of St Olaves parish and daughter of John Walker of Halifax, 15 February 1768 St Michael le Belfrey (YkCo 16 February 1768)

Sheriff 1772/3, JP North Riding (Wilson/140)

Declining business, stock for sale (YkCo 5 July 1774)

Jeweller, toyman, stock in trade for sale by auction (YChr 10 February 1775)

Continues business as auction was unsuccessful (YChr 3 March 1775)

Died at Exeter 11 May 1804 aged 76 (YkCo 21 May 1804)

Gower, Walter

Journeyman of Robert Gylmyn (q.v.), goldsmith, who paid 3s for his swearing an oath to the London company, 17 July 1573 (LGC Minute Book L/158–9)

Grant, Robert le

Goldsmith

Grant of his land in Walmgate in the parish of St Edward in the suburbs to Ralph de Waplington 1280 (BTC16/108)

Grant of his land in Walmgate in the parish of St Edward in the suburbs to Gaudin (q.v.) the goldsmith 20 July 1282 (BTC16/110)

Witness to a grant 6 November 1282 (BTC16/110)

Witness to a grant 1286/7 (BTC16/58)

Quitclaim made by his son Nicholas, chaplain, concerning a toft in Walmgate in the parish of St Edward in the suburbs 1 September 1317 (BTC16/116)

Grant, William*

Acquired the business of E. Epworth (q.v.), jeweller and goldsmith, 8 Spurriergate and opened in the premises. Branch in Lord Mayor's Walk (YG 8 April 1905)

Registered his mark, WG, as watchmaker and jeweller with Birmingham Assay Office 21 March 1911 (letter from librarian at Birmingham Assay Office)

Business, W. Grant & Son, closed (YEP 15 August 1973)

Grantham, John de

Goldsmith, Free 1377 (SS96/74)

Grantham, William de

Chamberlain 1306 (SS96/10)

Bailiff 1311/12 (YCA D1/290b)

Graundisson, Reg.

Goldsmith, Free 1398 (SS96/100)

Gray, Thomas (Gra, Graa)

Goldsmith, Free 1469 (SS96/189)

Lived in St Sampson's parish (RHS)

Member, with wife, Margaretta, of Corpus Christi Guild 1471 (SS57/80)

Admitted, with wife, Margaretta, member of Mercers' Guild 1480 (Cartulary/5b)

Chamberlain 1482 (SS96/203, Attreed/247)

Master of the episcopal mint within the Palace Garth 28 July 1487 (RHS)

Appointed as one of the arbiters in a dispute Robert Bayok, mercer and John Birkhede, mercer, 1488 (Attreed/604)

Sheriff 21 September 1488 (Attreed/623)

Provided some material for the weather vanes of the new bell tower of York Minster, 5s 10d, 1485 (SS35/88)

Alderman 3 March 1491 (RHS)

Constable of the Mercers' Guild 1492 (LRW/25)

MP for York 27 September 1495 (YCA B7/138)

Mayor 1497 (SS96/221)

In great decay and poverty, to have oversight of common wark and artillery, 5 June 1506 (YCA B9/34)

Resigned his gown as Alderman having fallen into great poverty, given a yearly allowance of 4 marks towards his living 5 May 1514 (YCA B9/76)

Greaves, William

Watchmaker of York 1730 (Dinsdale/57)

Watchmaker of Minster Yard (Dir 1787)

Of Bedale 1790 (Dinsdale/57) buried 2 July 1796 (Loomes/90)

Greenwood, William Francis *

Born 26 October baptised 3 November 1839 St Wilfrid's (PReg)

Son of William Greenwood, cabinet maker, Free by patrimony, as a cabinet maker, 27 June 1861 (Malden)

Wife, Emma, died July 1864 aged 23 (YG 23 July 1864)

Married Sarah, youngest daughter of Thomas Dobson of The Grange, Brandsby, 27 July 1865 Easingwold RC church (YG 29 July 1865)

Cabinet maker 24 Stonegate (Dir 1867)

Registered his mark (WFG) as W.F. Greenwood and Son, with Sheffield Assay Office 10 May 1895 (letter from librarian at Sheffield Assay Office)

Registered his mark (WFG) as W.F. Greenwood and Son, 23A and 24 Stonegate, York and 10 Royal Parade, Harrogate, with London Assay Office 2 September 1897 (Hulme 1/196, 2/314)

The Old Curiosity Shop, Stonegate, where one can purchase old furniture, china, silver and curios at reasonable prices (Mates Guide 1908)

Died 14 August 1915 buried York Cemetery grave 13524 MI (YCReg)

Grimesby, Richard de

Goldsmith, Free 1323 (SS96/21)

Of St Michael le Belfrey parish, paid poll tax of 3s on property valued at 60s 1327 (YASRS74/166)

Grimeston, Martin de

Goldsmith, witness to a grant of rent, 13th century (BTC16/131)

Grusey, Richard (Gruscy, Grushcy)

Goldsmith – one of two 'fit and prudent' goldsmiths appointed as assayers for York Mint, listed at the Trial of the Pix 2 March 1247/8 (Ellis/322)

Witness to an agreement 1250x1259 (YASRS148/100)

Witness to a grant January 1259 (YASRS148/103)

Witness to a confirmation of a grant January 1259 (YASRS148/104)

Witness to a quitclaim July 1261 (YASRS148/169)

Holder of a toft in Bootham, his heirs paid rent (husgabel) of 2s on it, 1284 (YAJ50/85)

Gulk, Herman de

Goldsmith, Free 1404 (SS96/108)

Guy

The goldsmith, grant of alms to the church of St Peter by his widow, Maud Postard 1220x1228 (YASRS148/286)

Gyllo, George

Goldfiner, son of Phillip Gyllo, mason, Free by patrimony 1559 (SS96/279)

Gylmyn, Nicholas (Gillmyn, Gilmyn)

Goldsmith of St Michael le Belfrey, indicted for recusancy, 26 July 1584 (Aveling/204)

Enjoined [to purge himself], 1586 (Aveling/206)

Goldsmith, son of Robert Gylmyn (q.v.), goldsmith (Free 1551), Free by patrimony 1589 (SS102/32)

Buried 31 August 1604 St Michael le Belfrey (PReg)

Gylmyn, Robert (Gylman) *1562–92

Goldsmith, son of William Gylmyn, merchant and [vintner], Free by patrimony 1550 (SS96/271)

Searcher 10 April 1561 (SS186/270, YCA B23/11b)

Present or former occupier of property in Monkgate 3 May 1562 (YASRS50/208 & 9)

Witness to a slander of the Lord Mayor 26 January 1562 (YCA B23/87)

Fined 2s 6d by the two wardens of the London company during their searches in the north, 5 February 1561 (LGC minute book K/176)

Chamberlain 1564 (SS102/5)

Wife, Mary, living in 1569 (RHS)

Swore an oath of good workmanship and paid 1s to the London company during their searches in the north. Also paid 3s each for the swearing of oaths by his apprentice, Thomas Taillour (q.v.), and his journeyman, Walter Gower (q.v.), 17 July 1573 (LGC minute book L/158–9)

Hague, Joshua

Jeweller of York married Anne Smith of Holy Trinity, King's Court, 29 December 1727 St Olaves (PReg)

Haiton, William

Goldsmith, son of William Haiton, milliner, Free by patrimony 1618 (SS102/68)

Haldesburgh, Harman

Goldsmith, Free 1476 (SS96/196)

Debts of 6s 8d each pending on chamberlains' accounts payable to Peter Couke, sergeant at mace, 24 June 1476 and to John Sponour, sergeant at mace, 30 November 1476. Both debts settled (Attreed/17 & 26)

Hall, George

Son of John Hall of York, apprenticed to James Barber (q.v.) and William Whitwell (q.v.), jewellers, indenture 4 October 1817, 7 years (YCA D16/16)

Hall, John Napoleon

Son of John Hall, pianoforte tuner, apprenticed to Christopher Watson (q.v.) and John Bell (q.v.), jewellers, indenture 25 August 1835, 7 years (YCA D16/169)

Jeweller of 103 Micklegate (Dir 1851), of Railway Street (Dir 1855), of 12 Micklegate (Dir 1861)

Jeweller and optician of Skeldergate married Frances Louisa, eldest daughter of Mr Cooper, gardener of York (YG 4 October 1856)

Silversmith, died of paralysis in the Union Workhouse 4 March 1870 buried York Cemetery grave 9867 (YCReg)

Hall, Robert

Goldsmith, son of Richard Hall, tailor, Free by patrimony 1633 (SS102/84)

Halton, Henry

Goldsmith, son of William Halton (q.v.), goldsmith, Free by patrimony 1434 (SS96/148)

Halton, Thomas de

Goldsmith, son of Robert de Halton, litster, Free by patrimony 1397 (SS96/99)

Halton, William

Goldsmith, father of Henry Halton (q.v.), goldsmith (Free by patrimony 1434)

Fined 22s 8d, payable to the chamberlains and the Goldsmiths' company, for making false money, 1417/18 (SS120/247)

Administration of will granted 27 June 1436 (YASRS6/78)

Hammond, Thomas Cundill

Son of George Hammond of Maumby, farmer, apprenticed to Henry Donkin Maltby (q.v.), clock and watchmaker, indenture 12 May 1818, 7 years (YCA D16/142)

Watchmaker, Free 1825 (Malden)

Wife, Jane, died at Richmond 1829 aged 26 (Loomes/93)

Watchmaker of Richmond 1830 (Poll)

Hampston, John *

Journeyman with Ambrose Beckwith, senior (q.v.), jeweller. With John Prince (q.v.) purchased the business from Beckwith's widow (YkCo 20 November 1770)

With his partner and William Clarke (q.v.) recommended to repair silver plate in the Mansion House, 25 February 1780 (YCA B45/12)

Wife, Margaret, died 21 August 1782 (YkCo 26 August 1782) MI St Laurence churchyard

George Cattle (q.v.) and Robert Cattle (q.v.) taken into partnership to form

Hampston, Prince and Cattles, c.1796 (HM)
Partner with John Prince (q.v.) in a glass manufactory in Fishergate, 1797
Died 26 January 1805 aged 66, dropsy, buried in St Laurence churchyard,
MI (PReg and YkCo 28 January 1805)
House in Fishergate for sale (YkCo 25 March 1805)

Hardy, Charles
Jeweller of 6 Coney Street (Dir 1830 and 1838)
Succeeded his father, John Hardy (q.v.), jeweller (YG 1 March 1834)
Seller of fishing tackle, bows and arrows, cricket bats etc., at the Ark, 6
Coney Street, closing down (YG 30 September 1843)

Hardy, John
Son of John Hardy of York, gentleman, apprenticed to John Langwith,
goldsmith, indenture 12 June 1721, 7 years (D13/1b)

Hardy, John
Jeweller, Free by order 1824 (Malden)
Purchases stock of Mrs M[artha] Marshall (q.v.) at her jewelry, turnery,
and cabinet warehouse at 6 Coney Street. Continues the business with the
help of his wife (YG 8 May 1824)
Has three medals struck (YG 30 May 1829)
Succeeded by his son Charles Hardy (q.v.) (YG 1 March 1834)

Hardy, Richard
Son of Richard Hardy, hairdresser (deceased) and Eleanor Hardy,
apprenticed to William Astley (q.v.), goldsmith, indenture 1 Aug 1799, 7
years (YCA D15/130)
Jeweller, Free 1806 (Malden)
Jeweller of Derby 1807 (Poll)
Died aged 26 (YkCo 8 April 1811)

Harlham, Hugh
Goldsmith, son of Warmebold de Harlham (q.v.), goldsmith (Free 1386),
Free by patrimony 1424 (SS96/135)
Possibly one of the two sons of Wermbolti [de Harlham] who were left
property in Stonegate by William Selar (q.v.), goldsmith 1402 (SRJ/4049
and 4050/1)

Harlham, Warmebold de (Arleham, Harlam, Harlaem) (Wamebold
                              Warymbolt, Wermbolti, Wormboldus, Wormod)
Goldsmith, Free 1386 (SS96/135) and coiner (YWCWG)
Valuer of the estate of Thomas Dalby, Archdeacon of Richmond, whose
will was proved in York in 20 May 1400 (Cripps/85)
Will of wife, Joanna, 14 September, proved 4 October 1401
(YASRS38/29) She left a knopped gold ring to John Aughoo (q.v.),
goldsmith (SS4/282)
Deed of feoffment of a messuage in Peter Lane the Little belonging to
William de Ottelay (gifted to him by Warmebold de Harlam) to
Warmebold and Laurencia, his wife, daughter of William de Selby of
York, 23 December 1406 (SS186/49)
Will of wife, Laurencia, 5 January 1407, proved 25 August 1408. To be
buried at St Michael le Belfrey (SS45/50)

Member, with wife, Agnes, of Corpus Christi Guild 1417/18 (SS57/19)
Deed of feoffment of messuage in Peter Lane the Little challenged in Council Chamber 6 October 1422. Other deeds were produced which Warmebold declared were false and not sealed with his accustomed seal of a *lion rampant* and with his initials on the circumference (SS186/49 and 50)
Father of Hugh Harlham (q.v.), goldsmith, Free by patrimony 1424 (SS96/135)
Owner of a tenement in Skeldergate, a messuage in Micklegate near Ousebridge and other property in Micklegate (YWCWG)
Will 28 April, administration granted 26 October 1430. Executor and legatee wife, Agnes. Employer of Robert Hydwyn (q.v.), goldsmith, supervisor of his will (YASRS6/79, YWCWG)
He had been the patron of a maison dieu in Peter Lane the Little (SS45/50)

Harper, John
Goldsmith, son of William Harper, draper, Free by patrimony 1544 (SS96/264)

Harrington, Christopher *1597–1615
Goldsmith, son of Anthony Harrington, tailor, Free by patrimony 1596 (SS102/39)
1604/5 paid 2s for putting a stone into the [city's] sword (Jewitt/454)
1605/6 paid 15s for silver and 5s for the labour of gilding the pendragon, hilt and pommel of the [city's] great sword (Jewitt/450)
  paid £5 for amending and altering the [city's] little sword (Jewitt/451)
  paid £9 19s for altering and mending the [city's] long sword

31½ ounces of silver at 5s the ounce		£7	17s	6d
for gilding every ounce at 2s the ounce		£3	3s	0d
making and working every ounce at 18d the ounce			47s	3d
For a white stone set in the cheape			2s	6d
	sum	£13	10s	3d
less for old silver at 5s the ounce		£4	9s	4d

(Jewitt/454)
Died 14 November 1614 buried St Martin, Coney Street, MI with arms of Goldsmiths' Company (PReg & YAJ18/54)
Will 11 November proved 22 December 1614 to be buried in his parish church near his children. Executor and legatee wife, Alice. Left seven plain gold rings, a gold ring set with five white sapphires, and a set of silver buttons for a doublet. Left a silver spoon worth 10s to the Goldsmiths' Company, his 'amellinge Morter and pestell and a paire of amellinge tonges' to 'my mann' James Plummer (q.v.), goldsmith, who had been apprenticed to him. All his other shop tools and other implements belonging to his craft were to be valued and his son, Robert, could have them, if he wished, at a reasonable rate, as part of the portion of the estate

due to him, After various bequests the residue of his estate were to be equally divided between his wife, Alice and his sons, Robert and Thomas. One of the witnesses was Thomas Waite (q.v.), goldsmith (YAJ18/55, Rel/213, YWCWG)

Father of Robert Harrington (q.v.), goldsmith, Free by patrimony 1617 (SS102/67)

Father of Thomas Harrington (q.v.), goldsmith, Free by patrimony 1625 (SS102/75)

Widow, Alice, buried 12 August 1649 St Martin, Coney Street (PReg)

HERE LIETH THE BODY OF, CHRISTOPHER HARINGTON OF THIS CITIE GOLD: SMITH, WHO DECEASED A°.DÑI.I 6 I 4

Harrington, Robert (Herrington) *1622–41

Goldsmith, son of Christopher Harrington (q.v.), goldsmith (Free 1595), Free by patrimony 1617 (SS102/67)

Bequests of 'my great bible' and a drawing book of six leaves of paper by his father's will in addition to his portion of the residuary estate which was to include any tools of the trade at valuation, 11 November 1614 (Rel/213)

Married Elizabeth, sister of James Plummer (q.v.) 6 July 1624 St Martin Coney Street (PReg)

Search of his shop made by two wardens of London company, 8 August 1635. Parcels of plate were removed which, upon assay on 10 August, were found to be substandard. After melting down or defacing raw material returned to him upon a fine and a pledge not to offend again (LGC Minute Book Si/259–266)

Chamberlain 1638 (SS102/90)

Buried 10 September 1647 St Martin, Coney Street (PReg)

Father of John Harrington, merchant, Free by patrimony 1652 (SS102/113)

Wife, Elizabeth, buried 14 February 1673 St Martin, Coney Street, under the bells (PReg)

Harrington, Thomas *1624–1641

Goldsmith, son of Christopher Harrington, goldsmith (Free 1595), Free by patrimony 1625 (SS102/75)

Bequest of 'my less bible' by his father's will in addition to his portion of the residuary estate, 11 November 1614 (Rel/213)

Search of his shop made by two wardens of London company, 8 August 1635. Parcels of plate were removed which, upon assay on 10 August, were found to be substandard. After melting down or defacing raw material returned to him upon a fine and a pledge not to offend again (LGC Minute Book Si/259–266)

Buried 23 December 1642 St Martin, Coney Street (PReg)

Will 11 December 1642 proved March 1642 (Rel/215)

Harrington, Thomas

Son of Thomas Harrington (q.v.), goldsmith, baptised 13 July 1627 St Michael le Belfrey (PReg)

Required under the terms of his father's will to 'elect or chuse otherly' to be educated by his uncle, Robert Harrington (q.v.), goldsmith. Additionally Robert was to bind him apprentice in his own or some other craft. If he failed to comply with these provisions he would 'not reepe or receive any benefitt' from the will, 11 December 1642 (Rel/215)

Harrison, Benjamin D.

Son of John Harrison (q.v.) engraver, apprenticed to John Prince (q.v.), Robert Cattle (q.v.) and George Cattle (q.v.), jewellers and silversmiths, indenture 23 January 1805, 8 years (YCA D15/187)

Goldsmith, jeweller, clock and watchmaker, apprentice and foreman with Barber, Cattle & Co of Coney Street for nearly 30 years – took over business of Matthew Hick (q.v.) deceased (YG 13 December 1834)

Silversmith and jeweller, died (YG 6 August 1836)

Harrison, John

Married Mary, daughter of the papist George Mattson, aledraper of Ogleforth c.1777. They had six children baptised at Blake Street chapel 1778–86. He took the Catholic Oath as a resident of the Liberty of St Peter 1792 (Aveling/383)

Engraver and copper plate printer of Coney Street (YH 16 March 1799)

Gave up independent business to become engraver to Hampston, Prince and Cattles, jewellers and silversmiths (YH 29 March 1800)

Married a daughter of the late Abraham Rowntree, surgeon (YkCo 28 March 1817)

Over 45 years principal artist to Barber, Cattle and North, jewellers and silversmiths, died aged 67 (YG 3 April 1830)

Harrison, John

Son of John Harrison (q.v.) engraver, apprenticed to Robert Cattle (q.v.)

and James Barber (q.v.), jewellers and silversmiths, indenture 5 November 1808, 7 years (YCA D15/225)

Assay at York 1817 (YAJ49/120)

Jeweller, Free 1818 (Malden)

Jeweller of Blossom Street 1818, of Monkgate 1820, of Coney Street 1830 (Poll)

Late foreman to Barber, Cattle & Co, 25 years experience there, 15 as principal workman, commenced business as working goldsmith, jeweller and chaser at 43 Coney Street, opposite the George Inn (YG 17 March 1832)

Moved from 43 Coney Street to 1 New Street (YG 19 October 1833)

Silversmith and jeweller, Blake Street (Dir 1834)

Harrison, John
Son of William Harrison, confectioner, apprentice to James Barber (q.v.) and William North (q.v.), jewellers and watchmakers, indenture 16 July 1836, 7 years (YCA D16/376)

Lately with Mr [James Silburn] Barber (q.v.) and his father [James Barber (q.v.)], opened business at 41 Low Petergate (YG 8 October 1859)

Harrison, Symond
Goldsmith, Free 1607 (SS102/55)

Hart, Robert
Watchmaker of 38 Pavement (Dir 1858), 3 High Petergate (Dir 1861), 17 Church Street (Dir 1866), 18 Church Street (Dir 1872) and 8 Market Street (Dir 1881)

Died 7 June 1888 aged 61 buried York Cemetery grave 6867 natural decay (YCReg)

Hartley, John
Clockmaker of Halifax, c.1775, and York, acquired the screw–cutting engine at the sale of the tools of Henry Hindley (q.v.), clockmaker, in 1774 (Law/207)

Harvey, Thomas
Son of Robert Harvey of York, innholder, apprenticed to James Bellamy Carill (q.v.), watchmaker and jeweller, indenture 7 May 1801, 7 years (D15/77)

Watchmaker, Free by order 1808 (Malden)

Watchmaker and jeweller of Stonegate (Dir 1809)

Watchmaker of Minster Yard 1830 (Poll)

Haunby, William de
Goldsmith, Free 1362 (SS96/56)

Chamberlain 1386 (SS/96/83)

Haukes, Thomas
Goldsmith, Free 1461 (SS96/180)

Paid 6d for gilding the mayor's mace 1642/3 (SS192/116)

Hawksworth, Walter
Apprenticed to William Thornton (q.v.) of York, clock and watchmaker, indenture 11 Feb 1760, 7 years, consideration £12, tax of 6s paid 10 April 1760 (PRO)

Still living in York in 1772 (Loomes/98)

Hayster, John (Haster)

Goldsmith, Free 1492, part of fee still owed [sum not mentioned] (SS96/216)

An alien and enfranchised man, to dwell in a Council tenement in Whipma–Whopmagate at a yearly rental of 20s, 20 March 1505 (YCA B9/32b)

Defects found in the parish of St Michael le Belfrey – John Hayster, goldsmith at the Minster steps has suspect persons drawing to their company in their shops at inconvenient times and especially one young girl, servant to a cooper in Fossgate, 1510 (SS35/262)

Goldsmith of Kirkham, will 23 November 1511 proved 20 March 1516 (YASRS/11/80)

Healey, Thomas

Son of John Healey of Manchester, watchmaker, apprentice to Henry Donkin Maltby (q.v.), indenture 27 May 1812, 7 years (YCA D15/265)

Heend, William (Heynde)

Goldsmith, Free 1431 (SS96/144)

Witness to a grant, 7 June 1464 (SS125/233)

Will 6 April proved 2 May 1467 to be buried in St Thomas' choir, St Michael le Belfrey. Left a silver gilt rose piece with a unicorn on the base, a goblet with a plain 'frounce' on the base, a silver spoon, and two gold rings. William Snawsell (q.v.), goldsmith, witness to and legatee of his will. (YASRS38/31, YWCWG)

Heidwyn, Thomas

Goldsmith, son of John Edwyn [sic], merchant (Free 1520), Free by patrimony 1551 (SS96/273)

Hesp, John

Son of William Hesp, joiner of York, apprenticed to James Barber (q.v.) and William North (q.v.), silversmiths, jewellers and engravers, indenture 9 June 1840, 7 years (YCA D16/401)

Hessay, Thomas

Goldsmith of York and London

Grantor of a tenement with shops and solars in Walmgate, 1366 (SRJ/2000)

Hemingway, John

Son of Richard Hemingway, blacksmith of York, apprenticed to William Topham (q.v.), jeweller, indenture 2 July 1790, 8 years (YCA D15/36)

Henrison, Richard

Jeweller, Free 1442 (SS96/160)

Henry

Goldsmith of St Michael, Spurriergate parish, paid poll tax of 12d on property valued at 20s 1327 (YASRS74/160)

Herford, William de

Goldsmith, Free 1310 (SS96/13)

Hertilpol, William de

Goldsmith, Free 1335 (SS96/29)

Heselgrave, Robert

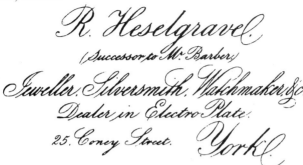

Son of Robert Heselgrave of Chapel Allerton, apprenticed to James Barber
(q.v.), George Cattle (q.v.) and William North (q.v.), jewellers, indenture
22 May 1830, 7 years (PRO)
Worked for 29 years with Barber & Co (YG 17 December 1859)
With Robert Walker (q.v.), another former employee, purchased Barber &
Co, 25/26 Coney Street (renumbered 13 by 1872) at auction (Gubbins/19)
Walker and Heselgrave, jewellers, silversmiths and watchmakers (YG 10
September 1859)
In business on his own (YG 17 December 1859)
Thomas Cooke (q.v.) moved to 26 Coney Street (YG 5 May 1860)
Silversmith of 25 Coney Street (Dir 1865) 12 Coney Street (Dir 1872)
Jeweller of 12 Coney Street, to retire (YG 1 January 1885)
Died 17 February 1885 aged 68 buried York Cemetery grave 14049,
cirrhosis of the liver (YCReg & YG 21 February 1885)
Widow, Margaret (q.v.) continued business at 40 Stonegate (YG 7 March
1885)

Heselgrave, Margaret

After the death of her husband, Robert (q.v.), and the sale of 12 Coney
Street she took premises at 40 Stonegate where she carried on the business
of jeweller in all its branches (YG 7 March 1885)
Jeweller and watchmaker, 40 Stonegate (Dir 1887), watchmaker (Dir 1890)
Of 26 Clarence Street died 21 March 1890 aged 72 buried York Cemetery
grave 14049 natural decay (YCReg & YG 22 March 1890)

Heselwood, Arthur Eastgate

Baptised 18 March 1850 St Maurice, son of Robert Massar Heselwood
(q.v.), watchmaker (HM)
Jeweller and silversmith, in business in Walmgate for preceding 12
months, receiving order issued (YG 4 July 1885) Notice of auction of his
stock and meeting of his creditors (YG 11 July 1885)
Watchmaker of 9 Haver Lane died 11 May 1895 aged 45 buried York
Cemetery grave 18855 heart disease (YCReg)

Heselwood, Charles

Watchmaker, baptised 17 December 1838 Lendal Chapel (PReg) son of

John Heselwood (q.v.), watchmaker, Free by patrimony 15 July 1861 (Malden)

Watchmaker and jeweller of 53 Goodramgate (Dir 1876, 1881, 1887, 1895, 1898)

[Continued his father's business]

Heselwood, Charles

Son of Robert Massar Heselwood (q.v.), bookseller then watchmaker (HM)

Watchmaker of March Street, died 26 August 1893 aged 31 buried York Cemetery grave 8281 paralysis (YCReg)

Heselwood, Charles

Watchmaker, born 26 December 1878 (HM), son of Charles Heselwood (q.v.) (Free 1861), watchmaker, Free by patrimony 28 May 1900 (Malden)

Heselwood, George Frederick

Baptised 8 July 1852 St Olave (HM), son of Robert Heselwood (q.v.), watchmaker, apprenticed to John Cundall Arundel (q.v.), watchmaker, indenture 21 June 1866, 7 years no consideration (YCA D17)

Watchmaker of 21 Charles Street, Free 22 April 1875 (Malden)

Watchmaker of 49 Bishophill (Dir 1876)

Watch and clockmaker, jeweller of 51 Coney Street (Dir 1881)

Continued the business of his uncle, Richard Heselwood (q.v.), watchmaker, who died 10 February 1877 (HM)

Died 17 January 1885 aged 33 buried York Cemetery grave 14917 MI pericarditis (YCReg & YG 20 January 1885)

His business taken over by George Norman Chapman (q.v.) (YG 9 May 1885)

Widow, Mary [daughter of George and Elizabeth Allan] of 41 Ratcliffe Street, died 2 May 1914 buried York Cemetery grave 14917 MI heart failure (YCReg)

Heselwood, John

Son of Thomas-Heselwood, grocer, baptised 26 December 1810 All Saints, Pavement (PReg) apprenticed to James Newbald (q.v.), watchmaker of York (Dinsdale/59)

Watchmaker, Free by patrimony 1835 (Malden)

Jeweller 53 Goodramgate (Dir 1843 & 1857) business founded 1839 (Dir 1881)

Wife, Harriet, died 19 January 1866 aged 60 buried York Cemetery grave 6485 MI disease of heart (YCReg & YG 27 January 1866)

Watchmaker of Heworth Road died 17 June 1873 aged 62 buried York Cemetery grave 6392 MI disease of the head, dropsy (YCReg)

[Business continued by his son, Charles Heselwood (q.v.), watchmaker]

Heselwood, Richard

Jeweller, son of Thomas Heslewood, grocer, Free by patrimony 17 July 1841 (Malden)

Watchmaker and jeweller of 1 Blake Street (Dir 1849)

Jeweller etc, death of wife Sarah at 43 Union Terrace 9 March 1856 aged 33 buried York Cemetery grave (public) 2167 epilepsy (YCReg & YG 15 March 1856)

Clock and watchmaker of 1 Blake Street (Dir 1857 & 1861)

Watchmaker of 51 Coney Street (Dir 1867), 53 Coney Street (Dir 1876)

Working goldsmith, second wife, Jane Goodrick Heselwood, died 27 June 1876 aged 53 buried York Cemetery grave 13853 (YCReg)

Silversmith of Coney Street died 10 February 1877 buried York Cemetery grave (private) 13853 pneumonia (YCReg & YG 17 February 1877)

[Business continued by his nephew, George Frederick Heselwood (q.v.), watchmaker]

Heselwood, Robert Massar

Watchmaker, son of Thomas Heselwood, grocer, baptised 20 June 1824 St Michael le Belfrey (PReg) Free by patrimony as a bookseller 19 June 1847 (Malden)

Died 5 October 1892 in the workhouse aged 68 buried York Cemetery grave 8281 phthisis (YCReg)

Father of Charles Heselwood (q.v.), watchmaker, died 26 August 1893 (HM)

Heulay, John de

Goldsmith, Free 1334 (SS96/28)

Heward, Christopher

Goldsmith, son of William Heward, vintner, Free by patrimony 1649 (SS102/108)

Hewitson, John

Goldsmith, Free 1607 (SS102/54)

Hick, Lambert

Son of George Hick of Gate Fulford, apprentice to John Armstrong (q.v.), watchmaker, indenture 13 February 1855, 7 years (YCA D16/503)

Hick, Matthew

Born 9 August baptised 18 September 1791 St Michael le Belfrey (PReg)

Watchmaker, son of Matthew Hick, whitesmith, Free by patrimony [18 August] 1812 (Malden)

Jeweller, clock and watchmaker of Minstergates (Dir 1818, 1823, 1830)

Chamberlain 1832 (RHS)

Watchmaker and jeweller of Minstergates died 23 October 1834 aged 43 (YG 25 October 1834)

Widow sold business to Benjamin D. Harrison (q.v.) (YG 13 December 1834)

Hields, John

Son of John Hields of York, aledraper, apprenticed to William Astley (q.v.), jeweller, indenture 21 October 1811, no term stated (YCA D15/257)

Goldsmith and jeweller, Free 1819 (Malden)

Goldsmith of 24 Pitt Street, Fitzroy Square, London 1820 & 1830 (Poll)

Hill, Jonah

Watchmaker of the Shambles

Son of William Hill, watchmaker of Cross Street, Hatton Garden, London by Piercy daughter of John West of London. Died 4 September at Mulwith by Boroughbridge, buried 8 September 1774 in the churchyard of St Olaves (PReg)

Hillensame, William
Goldsmith, Free 1371 (SS96/67)

Hillyard, Joseph
Silversmith, son of John Hillyard (Free 1830), miller, Free by patrimony 31 May 1841 (Malden)

Hindley, Henry
Of Manchester 1728 (Law/205)
Leased a house belonging to Thomas Gent, the printer, in Petergate for £7 a year (Gent2/192)
Clockmaker, Free by order 1732 (SS102/233) upon his making and presenting a very good and handsome eight day clock and case for the Lord Mayor's house and another for the Common Hall and taking care of them for one year, 9 March 1731 (YCA B42/153)
Clockmaker, Petergate (YkCo 24 December 1734)
Of St Michael le Belfrey, with wife, presented as papists 1735 (Aveling/270 & 374)
Moved to Stonegate 1741 (Gent2/197)
Bonded as a papist, not to move more than 5 miles from his residence without a licence, 11 October 1745 (Aveling/272)
Father of Joseph Hindley (q.v.), clock and watchmaker, Free by patrimony 1754 (SS102/273)
Papist, aged 67, 25 years resident in St Michael le Belfrey, 1767 (Aveling/283)
Watchmaker, Stonegate, house and shop to let (YkCo 16 May 1769)
Moves to house next door (YkCo 20 June 1769)
Died 23 March 1771 aged 71 (YkCo 26 March 1771)
Buried 25 March 1771 St Michael le Belfrey (PReg)
Business continued by his son, Joseph Hindley (q.v.) (YkCo 2 April 1771)
Tools and machines sold at public auction after the death of his son (YkCo 6 September 1774)

Hindley, Joseph
Son of Henry Hindley (q.v.), apprenticed to his father, indenture 1 September 1742, 7 years (YCA D13/99b)
Clock and watchmaker, Free 1754 (SS102/273)
Papist, aged 35, 25 years resident in St Michael le Belfrey, 1767 (Aveling/283)
Continued his father's business (YkCo 2 April 1771)
Died unmarried in Hull 4 March, buried there 7 March 1774 (YkCo 8 March 1774)

Hindley, Roger
Apprenticed to his brother, Henry Hindley (q.v.), clock and watchmaker, later watch cap maker of London (Setchell/40)

Hobart, Gabriel
Watchmaker, Petergate
Children baptised at St Michael le Belfrey 1751 & 1754 (PReg)

Hodgson, Mark
Watchmaker, Free 1676 (SS102/148)

Buried 26 February 1709 (Loomes/103)
Father of John Hodgson, Free by patrimony 1716 (SS102/213)

Hodgson, Robert
Baptised 6 September 1815 St Michael le Belfrey (PReg), son of Thomas Hodgson, plumber and glazier, and Mary, daughter of John Moiser (HM)
Jeweller, Free by patrimony 28 June 1839 (Malden)
Goldsmith, silversmith and jeweller, married Ann daughter of Mr Mouncer, currier (YG 22 June 1839)
Jeweller, purchased stock in trade of T & J Thompson (q.v.), jewellers, silversmiths and watchmakers of Minstergates (YG 11 March 1843)
Jeweller of 1 South Entrance, Minster Yard [Minstergates] (Dir 1843)
Died 5 February 1844 aged 28 buried York Cemetery grave 12455 consumption (YCReg)
Widow, Ann Hodgson (q.v.), continued business (YG 24 February 1844)

Hodgson, Ann
Daughter of John Mouncer, married Robert Hodgson (q.v.), goldsmith, silversmith and jeweller (YG 22 June 1839)
After death of her husband continued business (YG 24 February 1844)
Jeweller 81 Petergate [Minstergates corner] (Dir 1846)
Married secondly Joseph Cattaneo (q.v.), watchmaker of London (YG 30 October 1847)
Died 1 May 1848 aged 31 buried York Cemetery grave 12455 consumption (YCReg)

Holme, Thomas
Goldsmith, Free 1406 (SS96/109)

Holmes, John
Apprenticed to Henry Hindley (q.v.) c.1742–1749, lodging with John Smeaton in Great Turnstile, London, 1750, in business in Strand, London (Law/206)
Trustee, with William Clark (q.v.), John Smeaton and 2 others in York Waterworks, owned 3 shares of £250 each (out of 28), 12 October 1779 (Radley/151)
Purchased a further share in York Waterworks from John Smeaton for £400, 1788 (Radley/151)

Hopper, Arthur Edgar *
Watchmaker and jeweller, son of a Goole jeweller, established a business at 13 New Street, 1926 (YEP 11 November 1976)
Business traded at 32A Coney Street before moving to 6 Lendal in 1950 (YEP 16 March 1984)
Retired 1974 (YEP 21 April 1983)
Business, A.E Hopper & Son, continued by his son, John Christopher Hopper (YEP 12 November 1986)
Mark, AEH & S, registered with Sheffield Assay Office 3 October 1975 (letter from librarian at Sheffield Assay Office)
Died 21 April 1983 aged 84 (YEP April 1983)
Firm, now Hopper of York, 15 Lendal, sold to Stanley and Richard Gillan (YEP 16 March 1994)

Hopperton, Thomas (Hoperton)
Goldsmith, Free 1524 (SS96/245)
Chosen to be representative of his craft on the Common Council of the
city 13 February 1532/3 (YCA B11/144)

Hopperton, William
Goldsmith, Free 1539 (SS96/258)

Hopton, William
Son of George Hopton, corset maker, apprenticed to James Barber (q.v.)
and William North (q.v.), silversmiths and jewellers, indenture 4 February
1837, 7 years (YCA D16/432)

Horn, Herman
Goldsmith, Free 1431 (SS96/144)
In possession of a tenement belonging to Merchants' company in the area
of Ousegate, Skeldergate, Micklegate and Tofts at a rental of 4d a year,
1451 (SS129/57)

Horn, Richard
Goldsmith, member of Corpus Christi Guild 1446 (SS57/47)

Hornby, Thomas
Baptised 19 December 1756 St Crux (PReg)
Son of George Hornby, carpenter, apprenticed to John Hampston (q.v.) and
John Prince (q.v.), silversmiths and jewellers, indenture 26 February 1771,
7 years, consideration £20 (YCA D14/101)
Jeweller, Free by patrimony [21 December] 1778 (Malden)
Jeweller of Spurriergate 1784 (Poll)
Jeweller, died (YH 14 January 1792)

Horner, William
Son of John Horner of York, labourer, apprenticed to Edward Jackson
(q.v.), jeweller and silversmith, indenture 1 May 1822, 7 years (YCA
D16/97)

Hornesey, Roger
Goldsmith, Free 1601 (SS102/46)

Hornsey, Thomas Edward
Son of Thomas Hornsey of York, tobacconist, apprenticed to Joshua Potts
(q.v.), clock and watchmaker, indenture 11 November 1814, 7 years, no
consideration (YCA D15/292)
Watchmaker, Free 1826 (Malden)
Watchmaker of Goodramgate 1830 (Poll)
Watchmaker, 9 St Andrewgate (Dir 1855)
Died 17 April 1859 aged 65 buried York Cemetery grave 3489 jaundice
(YCReg)

Horseley, Cornelius
Watchmaker, son of Edward Horseley, Free by patrimony 1656
(SS102/119)
Married Elizabeth Hunt 1665 Northampton (Loomes/105)
Fined 10s for attending a Quaker meeting and had goods to that value
taken from him. (Dinsdale/61)
Died 1681, administration of estate granted 1682. Widow, Elizabeth, died

1693 (Loomes/105)

Horsfall, William

Watchmaker, 1 Blake Street (Dir 1846)

Admitted to N & E Riding Lunatic Asylum, Clifton. Died 12 June 1847 age 42 buried York Cemetery grave 2403 found drowned (YCReg)

Horsman, Thomas

Son of Thomas Horsman of York, apprenticed to James Barber (q.v.), George Cattle (q.v.) and William North (q.v.), jewellers, indenture 22 May 1830, 7 years (YCA D16/264)

Silversmith, Free 20 May 1839 (Malden)

Houison, James Branch

Watch and clockmaker, College Street (Dir 1834) 12 Spurriergate (Dir 1838, 1841)

Jeweller, watch and clock maker, and dealer in coins, 25 Spurriergate (Dir 1843)

Hovingham, William de (Hovyngham)

Goldsmith, Free 1357 (SS96/52)

Received £10 in part payment of the price of a silver dish bought from him to lay alms in at our table, 14 September 1360 (Fasti Ebor 6/400)

Leased Mulberry Hall, Stonegate, grant by Robert de Wykfork, prebendary of North Newbald 1370–5, 5 January 1371 (Drake App/lxii)

Bailiff 1371/2 (Drake/361)

Mentioned in the inventory of John de Scardeburgh, goldsmith (q.v.), 1402 (Borthwick, D&C Cause papers 1402/1)

Legate of the will, 18 January 1402, of William Selar (q.v.), goldsmith (YWCWG)

Howe, Thomas

Servant to Thomas Symson (q.v.), goldsmith, who paid 3s for his swearing an oath to the London company, 17 July 1573 (LGC Minute Book L/158–9)

Goldsmith, Free 1577 (SS102/19)

Howsold, James

Goldsmith, Free, 1543 (SS96/263)

Hoy, George

Watchmaker, married Betty Miller, widow, 22 November Holy Trinity, Goodramgate (PReg)

Watchmaker, Free by order 1808 (Malden)

Watchmaker, Petergate, house for sale (YkCo 25 July 1808)

Of Micklegate (Dir 1818)

Death aged 61 (YCh 4 February 1819)

Business continued by his widow, Elizabeth (Dir 1823)

Hudson, Robert

Ordered to assist Robert Beeforth (q.v.) in gathering together all the materials of the old clock and chimes at York Minster, 23 June 1658 (YCA B/113)

Hudson, William

Son of Mark Hudson, saddler, baptised 28 December 1700, St Michael le

Belfrey (PReg), apprenticed to John Langwith (q.v.), goldsmith, indenture 1 September 1715, 7 years, consideration £20 (PRO)

Silversmith, Free by patrimony 1722 (SS102/221)

Of St Michael le Belfrey, with wife presented as papists, 1735. He had converted Mrs Ogle whom he had married 6/7 years previously (Aveling/270)

Hugh

The goldsmith

Witness to a grant 8 May 1290 (YASRS148/237)

Witness to grants 31 May & 21 September 1292 (YASRS148/10 & 295)

His son, Hugh, paid poll tax of 5s 4d, 1301 (YASRS21/120)

Hull ,John

Son of James Hull of York, vintner, apprenticed to William Peacock (q.v.), watchmaker of St Michael, Spurriergate, parish, indenture 17 July 1792, 7 years, consideration £20 10s 0d (PRO)

Watchmaker, College Street (Dir 1823)

Hundmanby, William de

Goldsmith, Free 1350 (SS96/43)

Huntes, Robert

Goldbeater, Free 1350 (SS96/42)

Hunton, Christopher *1566–70

Goldsmith, Free 1551 (SS96/272)

Of Stonegate, mentioned in the will, 10 September 1560, of Martin Soza (q.v.), goldsmith (YWCWG)

Fined 21s for a faulty assay by the two wardens of the London company during their searches in the north, 5 February 1561 (LGC minute book K/176)

Supervisor of will, 15 January 1566, and guardian of the two children of Richard Wawton (q.v.), goldsmith (YWCWG)

Died 1582 (Jackson/297)

Father of Hugh Hunton, tailor, Free by patrimony 1587 (SS102/29)

Hurworth, Lewis

Baptised 3 August 1804 IBVM and Holy Trinity, Micklegate, son of Thomas Hurworth of Micklegate, stay–maker, and Elizabeth Cromack (PReg)

Married Mary, only daughter of Edward Woods of the Nag's Head, Micklegate, 7 December 1828 St Olaves (PReg)

Jeweller, Free by patrimony 1830 (Malden)

Working jeweller 3 Stonegate (Dir 1830) of Ogleforth (Dir 1834)

Died at Sheffield aged 42 (YG 19 April 1846)

Huchonson, Robert (Huchynson)

Goldsmith, Free 1479 (SS96/201)

Debts of 40d pending on chamberlains' accounts payable to John Sponer, sergeant at mace, March 1479 and to John Hardwyk, sergeant at mace, January 1479. Both debts settled (Attreed/187 & 190)

Chamberlain 1498 (SS96/222)

Will 12 March 1506, no date for probate, to be buried next to his wife's tomb in St Michael, Spurriergate. Executor and legatee wife, Sisle. Churchwardens of St Michael, Spurriergate, to have his house if his daughter, Janet, died without heirs. All the tools in his shop left to his friend and apprentice, John Marshall (q.v.) (YASRS6/90, YWCWG)

Hutchenson, William

Goldsmith, son of William Hutchonson (q.v.), goldsmith (Free 1572), Free by patrimony 1605 (SS102/50)

Hutchonson, William (Hutchenson) *1593

Goldsmith, son of Thomas Hutchonson, locksmith, Free by patrimony 1572 (SS102/13)

Father of William Hutchenson (q.v.), goldsmith, Free by patrimony 1605 (SS102/50)

Hutton, Thomas

Third son of Matthew Hutton of Priest Hutton, Lancashire (YAJ6/opp 238)

Goldsmith, Free 1569 (SS102/10) for 40s 0d at the contemplation of his brother, Matthew Hutton, Dean of York (YAJ6/opp 238)

Swore an oath of good workmanship and paid 5s to the London company during their searches in the north, 17 July 1573 (LGC minute book L/158–9)

Chamberlain 1573 (SS102/13)

Buried 7 July 1576 aged c.42 buried in York Minster (St Michael le Belfrey PReg)

Will 19 April proved 24 November 1576, to be buried in York Minster, Executor and legatee wife, Ann. Legatees William Rawnson (q.v.), goldsmith, and his wife (YASRS38/34, YWCWG)

Hyckes, Christopher

Goldsmith of York living in the Cathedral Close, administration of estate granted 29 July 1579 (YASRS38/34)

Hydwyn, Robert (Hidwyn)

Employed by Wamebold Harlham (q.v.), goldsmith at the time of his death in 1430 (YWCWG)

Goldsmith, Free 1431 (SS96/144)

Member, with his wife, Katherine, of Corpus Christi Guild 1433 (SS57/34)

Inglis, James Brown

Son of Hugh Inglis, born in Edinburgh in 1858 and trained as an engraver. Worked for Buller, Hutchinson & Co, Goldsmiths' Building, London. Married Anne Coates of Market Weighton c.1885. Opened a shop in the Market Place there selling boots and melodeons and a few years later another selling fancy jewellery and gifts. (YEP 3 November 1966)

Heraldic engraver 4 Spurriergate (Dir 1887)

Jeweller Clifford Street (1893 Dir) 4 Coney Street (Dir 1896)

Works 6 Castlegate [Crown Plating Works] (Dir 1909)

Elected Councillor (Independent), Guildhall Ward 1904 (YG 29 October 1904)

Re–elected Councillor (Conservative) Guildhall Ward (YG 5 November 1910)

Sheriff 1911/2 (YG 11 November 1911)

Alderman July 1914 (11 July 1914)

Wife, Anne died 24 Jan 1919 buried Fulford Cemetery MI (YG 1 February 1919)

Governor Merchant Adventurers' Company 1920–21 (Merch Adv Co)

Lord Mayor 1922

Married Sarah Freeman April 1923 (YG 23 April 1923)

Business closed temporarily June 1941 (YEP 3 November 1966)

Died 17 October 1942 buried Fulford Cemetery MI (HM)

Wife Sarah died May 1948 aged 87 buried Fulford Cemetery (HM)

Ipswich, John de

see Yppeswyche, John de

Jackson, Edward *

Son of John Jackson of York, tailor, apprenticed to John Hampston (q.v.), John Prince (q.v.), Robert Cattle (q.v.) and George Cattle (q.v.), jewellers and silversmiths, indenture 11 March 1799, 8 years, no consideration (YCA D15/125)

Jeweller of Bootham, Free 1807 (Malden)

Working jeweller, goldsmith and plate manufacturer, having conducted the working department of Cattle and Barber for 8 years and lately been in London, set up in business on his own (YCh 27 February & 24 July 1817)

Assays at York 1817–1821 (YAJ49/120)

Working jeweller, goldsmith and clockmaker, Coney Street (Dir 1818)

Elected Councillor Micklegate ward (YCh 21 January 1819)

Succeeded in shop by William Furnish, draper (YG 17 March 1821) but kept the workshop behind (Gubbins/19)

Goldsmith and silver plate manufacturer, working jeweller, manufacturer of mourning rings etc., 14 Coney Street (Dir 1823)

Bankrupt and his entire property put up for auction (YG 10 July 1824 & Gubbins/19)

Jeweller, goldsmith and silver plate manufacturer, 14 Coney Street (Dir 1830, 1838)

Silversmith, jeweller and fancy hair worker, 14 Coney Street (Dir 1834)

Jackson & Co, Berlin rooms for fancy wools, silks, canvasses, gold, silver and gilt tassels, cords, braids, needles &c. baby linen repository, also jeweller, 15 Coney Street (Dir 1843)

Branch of Berlin Rooms in High Harrogate, 1844 (Gubbins/20)

Goldsmith of Coney Street died 5 October 1859 aged 73 buried York Cemetery grave 11826 natural decay (YCReg and YG 8 October 1859)

Jackson, John

Watchmaker, married Sarah Prest 13 July 1789 St Michael le Belfrey (PReg)

Jackson, Richard

Clock and watchmaker, former pupil of Henry Hindley (q.v.), clockmaker, went to Hexham and opened a shop there in 1762 (Loomes/110)

James, Jeremiah

Apprenticed to Henry Hindley (q.v.), clock and watchmaker, 1755 (Setchell/50)

Jameson, Alexander
Goldsmith, son of William Jameson, yeoman, Free by patrimony 1496 (SS96/221)

Jocenia
Goldsmith
Son, Thomas, witness to a grant, made early in 13th century (YASRS148/145)

Jocelin, John (Joclin, Gocelin, Gocelyn, Goscelin)
Goldsmith
Witness to grants 1250x1299 (YASRS148/149), before October 1265 (YASRS148/172)
Bailiff 1259/60 (YASRS148/100 & 171)
Notice that he was one of the witnesses to a quitclaim 1269 (YASRS148/227)

John
Goldsmith
Witness to a document, 13th century (SRJ/1673)
Mentioned in undated documents (SRJ/483 & 1055)

Johnston, Alexander
Apprenticed to William Etherington (q.v.), jeweller, goldsmith etc., indenture 1 January 1788, 5 years, consideration £40 (PRO)

Johnson, Dirik
Goldsmith, Free 1424 (SS96/134)

Johnson, Francis
Goldsmith, known in 1590 (Jackson/298)

Johnson, George
Son of Joseph Johnson, saddler, apprenticed to Robert Cattle (q.v.) and James Barber (q.v.), jewellers and silversmiths, indenture 1 January 1810, 7 years (YCA D16/39)
Jeweller, Free 1818 (Malden)
Jeweller of Petergate 1818 & 1820 (Poll)
Chamberlain 1825 (RHS)

Johnson, Henry
Apprenticed to John Colayne (q.v.), goldsmith, Free 1484 (SS96/207)

Johnson, John
Son of Robert Johnson of York, apprenticed to Joseph Richmond (q.v.), clockmaker, indenture 26 November 1811, 7 years (YCA D15/275)

Johnson, William
Watchmaker, son of William Johnson, locksmith, Free by patrimony 1665 (SS102/131)
Father of William Johnson, Free by patrimony 1714 (SS102/210)

Jones, Mr
Of York. Appeared before the court of the London company for selling gold rings worse than the standard. Ordered to pay 34s , the cost of the goods, and charges of £1 12s 6d, 3 May 1700 (LGC Court Book 10/213)

Jones, Robert
Son of Josiah Jones of [Church Lane], Hull, goldsmith, apprenticed to

John Hampston (q.v.) and John Prince (q.v.), goldsmiths and jewellers, indenture 22 January 1782, 7 years, consideration £100 (YCA D14/274)
Married Ann Breary, daughter of Mr Breary of Tadcaster (YH 18 August 1798)
Of Tadcaster, assay at York 1806 (YAJ49/120)
Death of widow, Ann, aged 83 (YG 8 January 1859)

Jonyn (Genyn)
Goldsmith, valuer of the estate of Thomas Dalby, Archdeacon of Richmond, whose will was proved in York on 20 May 1400 (Cripps/85)
Probably John (Jamin) Aughoo (q.v.)
Goldsmith of Stonegate
For gilding three thuribles and making chains for them using 24 ounces of silver for York Minster, 66s 10d, for making windows for the thuribles with chains and frames for the windows, one with gold, and gilding them, £4 3s 5d. Total £7 [10s] 3d, 1405 (SS35/133)

Jordan
The goldsmith
Mentioned in a grant as holder of land in Glovergail (Church Street) owned by Ralph le Furbur, before 1260 (YASRS38/65)

Joy, Thomas
Jeweller, son of Thomas Joy, aledraper, Free by patrimony 31 May 1841 (Malden)
Jeweller of 57 Stonegate (Dir 1843)

Kenlay, John de
Goldsmith
Will of wife, Alice, 8 August 1362 proved 28 June 1364 (YASRS38/36)
Grantor of a messuage with garden in Bootham 1368 (SRJ/845)
Of All Saints, Pavement parish, paid poll tax of 3s 0d with wife Katerina, 1381 (Bartlett/25)

Kidd, William
Born 7 baptised 13 August 1769 St Martin, Coney Street (PReg)
Son of Matthew Kidd, victualler deceased (Free by order 1762), and Isabella, his wife, apprenticed to Richard Clark (q.v.), goldsmith, indenture 9 December 1782, 8 years (YCA D14/238)
Jeweller of Wakefield, Free by patrimony 4 January 1802 (Malden)
Jeweller of Wakefield 1807 (Poll)

Kidson, William
Clockmaker, Free 1615 (SS102/63) commended by divers Knights and others of good worth to be verie skilful in the art or science of making silver clocks or watches. Now in that there is not any within this city that is skilful or perfect in making or amending them therefore this Court is well pleased to bestow the Freedom of this city upon him without paying any money for the same. He offered to give the Corporation a clock, 18 January 1614 (YCA B34/48b)
The company of Locksmiths agreed that Kidson should not exercise their trade in any way, publicly or privately, but it was lawful for him to make, mend or repair clocks, watches or dials, or everything pertaining to that

occupation but no other, 12 May 1615 (YCA B34/60b)
Kipling, William
Apprenticed to Henry Hindley (q.v.), clockmaker, indenture 8 August 1758, 7 years. Tax of an unspecified amount paid on 16 February 1762 (PRO)
Kirby, Rowland (Kerby) *1669–80
Goldsmith, Free 1669 (SS102/134)
Six silver boats bought from him by Edward Malt on behalf of Major John Wallis who, on 17 May 1671, claimed expenses of £8 1s 1d from the wardens of the London company. These expenses included other items bought from Robert Williamson (q.v.) and Thomas Mangy (q.v.) as well as carriage and letters (LGC Court Book 6/196–7)
Kirk, James (Kirke, Kyrk)
Goldsmith, late apprentice to Thomas Welles (q.v.), Free 1482 on payment of 5s to the use of the city and 12d to the Common Clerk and the mayor's esquires [sword and mace bearer] (SS96/204)
With others stood surety for William Baker, clerk, to do no damage or bodily harm to any of the king's subjects, undated but c. 1486 (Attreed/448)
With John Lowas of Tadcaster, gentleman, accepted bond (ultimately voided) to accept arbitration in a dispute between them, 21 November 1487 (Attreed/596)
Admitted, with wife, member of Mercers' Guild, 1490 (Cartulary/12)
With George Kirk, merchant, stood surety that Richard Smales, rector of All Saints, North Street, would do no damage or bodily harm to John Rayner, chaplain, 9 April 1489 (Attreed/636)
Will 7 April proved 8 August 1515, to be buried in the choir before the altar in St Crux. Executor and legatee wife, Margaret (YASRS11/103, YWCWG)
Kirk, Thomas
Goldsmith, known in 1479 (Jackson/297)
Kirkeby, John
Goldsmith, Free 1442 (SS96/160)
Kitchin, George (Kytchyng, Kitcheinge) *1570–94
Goldsmith, Free 1562 (SS102/4)
Chamberlain 1567 (SS102/8)
Swore an oath of good workmanship and paid 3s to the London company during their searches in the north. Also paid 3s each for the swearing of oaths by his servants William Pearson (q.v.), Nicholas Kitchin (q.v.) And his journeyman James le Shockie, a Frenchman, 1572 (LGC minute book L/158–9)
Of Bootham ward, representative of the goldsmiths' craft on the Common Council of the city, May 1579 (YCA B27/160b)
In occupation of a house on land to the north of the Guildhall, August 1582 (YCA B27/178b)
Son, Thomas Kitchin (q.v.) baptised 13 September 1582 St Martin, Coney Street (PReg)
Presented by the searchers of the craft to the Lord Mayor for selling plate

which had not been assayed and working impure silver, 15 February 1582 (YCA B28/91b)

Fined £8 6s 8d without any mitigation or forgiveness and also to remake the plate with good silver, 1 March 1582 (YCA B28/93)

Informed the council that William Pearson (q.v.) and Thomas Waddie (q.v.), searchers, had refused to mark his plate with the touch, 10 May 1583 (YCA B28/97)

Paid £5 of his fine, the balance of £3 6s 8d was by agreement given him again, 17 May 1583 (YCA B28/98b)

To go, with John Yedall [Yodale], macebearer, to every goldsmith's shop in York and get one parcel of plate from each of them, 7 June 1583 (YCA28/101b)

With another goldsmith and such citizens appointed by the Lord Mayor to take the parcels of silver to London to be tried by the assay master of the London company, 14 June 1583 (YCA B28/103)

Award of arbitrators appointed to decide on his disputes with his fellow goldsmiths, Thomas Waddy (q.v.), William Pearson (q.v.), John Stock (q.v.), John Raylton (q.v.) and Martin Byggyn (q.v.) 25 October 1583 (YCA B28/114)

Of St Martin, Coney Street parish, contributor in 1590 of £20 towards a loan to Queen Elizabeth (Cartwright/374)

Wife, Ann, buried St Laurence 23 May 1591 (PReg)

Buried St Martin, Coney Street 21 July 1597 (PReg)

Will 13 July proved 26 September 1597, to be buried in the south choir in St Martin, Coney Street. Left a sealing ring with onyx stone, two little rings which he wore, two gold rings each of half an angel weight, and a gold ring with a white stone and all the tools of occupation to his son, Thomas Kitchin (q.v.)(YASRS24/62, YWCWG)

Kitchin, Nicholas (Kytchen)

Servant of George Kitchin (q.v.), goldsmith, who paid 3s for his swearing an oath to the London company, 17 July 1573 (LGC Minute Book L/158–9)

Goldsmith of London, 13 July 1597 (YWCWG)

Kitchin, Thomas

Baptised 13 September 1582 St Martin, Coney Street, son of George Kitchin (q.v.) (PReg)

Apprenticed to George Kitchin (q.v.), his father, c.1595, aged 15 in 1597. His father requested in his will, 13 July 1597, that Anthony Bates [St Vedast parish], Nicholas Kitchin (q.v.) and Richard Walker [St Peter, Westcheap, parish], London goldsmiths, place him with an honest goldsmith in London to complete his term for three or four years. His father left him his tools and rings. (YWCWG)

Goldsmith, Free by patrimony 1604 (SS102/49)

Kleiser, Andrew

Clock and watchmaker, born Schollach, Schwarzwald, Baden (1881 Census)

Employed by Philip Schwerer, clockmaker, 38 Stonegate (1841 Census)

With Augustine Kleiser (q.v.) purchased the business in 1842 (YG 30 May 1846)

Naturalisation papers dated September 1852 (YG 22 October 1853)

Clock and watchmaker, 39 Stonegate, 23 years in business (YG 14 February 1863)

Also at 22 Parliament Street (1881/2 Dir)

Died 4 January 1885 aged 65 buried York Cemetery grave 12283 angina pectoris (YCReg)

After his death the shop in Stonegate was closed and the business moved to Parliament Street (YG 21 February 1885)

Wife, Hannah [Potter, born Church Fenton] died 21 December 1898 buried York Cemetery grave 12283 natural decay (YCReg)

Kleiser, Augustine

Clockmaker, 38 Stonegate, aged 35 working for Philip Schwerer (q.v.) (1841 Census)

With Andrew Kleiser (q.v.) purchased the business of P Schwerer in 1842 (YG 30 May 1846)

Kleiser, Joseph

Clock and watchmaker of Stonegate, taken into partnership by his brother, Andrew Kleiser (q.v.) by 1857 (YAYAS34/6 and Dir 1857)

Married, Mary, fourth daughter of the late Henry Potter of Osbaldwick, farmer (YG 4 March 1854)

Naturalised British subject (1861 Census)

Died 29 December 1885 aged 62 buried York Cemetery grave 12154 phthisis (YCReg)

Wife, Mary, died 10 October 1992 aged 68 York Cemetery grave 12154 bronchitis (YCReg)

Kleiser, Martin

Watchmaker, aged 18, born Schollach, Germany, visiting his brother Andrew Kleiser (q.v.) (1851 Census)

Traded at 14 Stonegate as M. Kleiser & Co having, by 1861, purchased the business of Matthew Schwerer (q.v.) (YAYAS34/7)

Schwerer and Kleiser, 14 Stonegate (Dir 1867)

M. Kleiser & Co, clockmakers, 12 Stonegate, under management of Bernard Tritschler, watchmaker and dealer in jewellery (1871 Census) and eventually became M. Wehrly & Co, watch and clockmakers, jewellers etc. (YG 14 July 1883)

Kleiser, Otmar

Watchmaker of 24 Parliament Street (Dir 1861) aged 30, born in the Grand Duchy of Baden. Wife, Louisa, aged 28, born in Germany (1861 Census)

Died 21 May 1866 aged 38 buried York Cemetery grave 14154 phthisis (YCReg)

Business continued by his wife, Louisa (born Wolland, Dorset, aged 47 in 1881), until she married Henry J. Newton (q.v.) on 3 February 1874. After which she transferred to his name (YAYAS34/7 and YG 21 February 1874)

Lamspring, Bartholomew
Goldsmith, Free 1468 (SS96/187)
Lancaster, Mr
Watchmaker of St Michael le Belfrey, with wife presented as papists, 1735 (Aveling/270)
Langlathorp, John
Free 1364 as a girdler (SS96/53)
Goldsmith, once occupier of a tenement in Stonegate, now in the occupation of Cissote de Marton, rent paid 24s per annum, 11 March 1421 (SS120/75)
Langwith, Benjamin
Baptised 23 August 1708 York Minster (PReg) and 31 August 1708 St Michael le Belfrey (PReg)
Third son of John Langwith (q.v.), goldsmith, apprenticed to Wilfrid Tolson (q.v.) of York, jeweller, indenture 26 February 1720, 8 years (YCA D13/13b)
Langwith, James
Watchmaker, son of Oswald Langwith, gentleman, clerk of the vestry, York Minster, and brother of John Langwith (q.v.), goldsmith (RHS)
Married Elizabeth, daughter of John Denton, 5 March 1716 York Minster (PReg)
Father of Oswald Langwith baptised 27 June 1722 St Michael le Belfrey (PReg)
Buried 7 February 1722 aged 32 St Maurice (PReg)
Widow, Elizabeth married second John Fryer as his first wife 21 January 1724 York Minster (see also Langwith, John) (PReg)
Langwith, John *1702–21
Goldsmith, Free 1700 (SS102/182)
Son of Oswald Langwith, gentleman, clerk of the vestry, York Minster, and brother of James Langwith (q.v.), watchmaker (RHS)
Aged 25 in 1704, marriage bond with Lucy Mitton (YASRS46/122) whom he married 12 August 1704 St Olave (PReg)
Chamberlain 1712 (SS102/198)
On closure of York Assay Office in 1716 arranged to have his work assayed at the Newcastle upon Tyne office (Lee/9)
'Rec'd by Mr Shaw of John Langwith of York goldsmith for Essay for one year ending 1 Augt 1717 20s pd into ye box' (Gill/152)
'Head Meeting day May 4th 1719 John Langwith of Yorke dt. for Essay one year due Lammas 1718 20s Mr Shaw to make good the same if not pd' (Gill/152)
By Mr White for Mr Langwiths Essay for 1718 01:00:00 Mar 7 1719 (Gill/152)
By Mr Langwiths Essay mony for the year 1719 01:00:00, 3 May 1720 (Gill/152)
One year Essay 20s, 3 May 1721 (Gill/152)
To be called upon for 20s for a years Essay due Lammas last, 3 May 1722 (Gill/152)

Died intestate 1723 administration of estate granted 8 March 1723 (RHS)
Widow, Lucy, married 23 May 1727 York Minster John Fryer of York as
his second wife (See also Langwith, James) (PReg)
Father of Benjamin Langwith (q.v.)
Father of Oswald Langwith, mariner, Free by patrimony 1736 (SS102/244)
Father of George Langwith, mercer and clothdresser, Free by patrimony
1740 (SS102/252)
Father of Edward Langwith, Free by patrimony 1740 (SS102/253)
Father of John Langwith, Free by patrimony 1741 (SS102/260)
Father of Martin Langwith of Bramhope, yeoman, Free by patrimony 1758
(SS102/285)

Leake, William
Jeweller, son of William Leake, innholder, Free by patrimony 1741
(SS102/258)
Jeweller of Leeds 1758 (Poll)

Lee, Henry *1675
Goldsmith, son of Henry Lee, miller, Free by patrimony 1675 (SS102/147)
Father of William Lee, Free 1704 (SS102/188)

Lee, Richard
Assayer York Mint, beneficiary of (a black gown and a fox furred gown)
and witness to the will of Richard Ugdon, Master of the York Mint, 8 May
1545 (SS106/226 & 227)

Lendard, Medardus
Goldsmith, Free 1452, owed 16s 8d (SS96/171)

Levy, Samuel
Son of Henry Levy, glass cutter, apprenticed to John Hampston (q.v.) and
John Prince (q.v.), jewellers, indenture 19 May 1785, 7 years (YCA
D14/274)
Jeweller, Free 1792 (Malden)

Lewis, David
Clockmaker of Knaresborough
Four children baptised at St Crux between 1766 and 1771 (PReg)

Lion, Charles
Clockmaker, son of Matthew Lion of Hamilton, Scotland, farmer, married
to Susannah daughter of George Stilling of Cawood, joiner. Their first
child and daughter, Ann, born 1 baptised 10 December 1787 Holy Trinity,
King's Court (PReg)

Lorfever, Henry
Witness to a grant 17 February 1319 (YASRS148/134)

Lorfever, Jeremy
Grant of land and buildings in Fossgate from Mariota, daughter of Ellen,
late wife of Paulinus the goldsmith (q.v.) of York, to Jeremy Lorfever and
Agnes his wife, 1286/7 (BTC16/57 & 58)

Lowvell, John (Lovell)
Goldsmith, Free 1375 (SS96/73)
Of St Mary, Castlegate parish, orlogemaker, paid poll tax with wife Agnes,
1381 (Bartlett/19)

Lunde, John (Londe, Lounde, Lund, Lunde)

Goldsmith, Free 1542 (SS96/262), born Kirkby Overblow (YAJ57/120)
Witness to the will of Oswald Chapman (q.v.), goldsmith (YWCWG)
Chamberlain 1549 (SS96/268) Will 10 August proved 10 October 1558 witnessed by his brother in law, Richard Bargeman (q.v.), goldsmith, husband of his sister, Elizabeth. To be buried within his parish church of Holy Trinity, Goodramgate. Executor and residuary legatee his, Isabel (Reg. Test. 15/3 132b, YWCWG)

Luneburgh, John

Goldsmith

Will 13 August proved 17 December 1458 to be buried at St Helen, Stonegate near his first wife, Elizabeth. Left 6s 8d to the goldsmiths' craft to complete a gold crown. Bequeathed 20d and some tools to Robert Spicer (q.v.), goldsmith, and some tools to John Pudsay (q.v.), goldsmith. Left silver goblet with cover, silver bowl worth 20s 0d, and a piece of silver worth 5 marks. Executor and legatee second wife, Agnes (YASRS6/107, SS30/213, YWCWG)

Lupton, William

Clockmaker, Free 1646 (SS102/102)
Watchmaker, buried 9 November 1680 St Martin, Coney Street (PReg)
Father of William Lupton (q.v.), clockmaker, Free by patrimony 1681 (SS102/156)

Lupton, William

Clockmaker, son of William Lupton (q.v.), clockmaker (Free 1646), Free by patrimony 1681 (SS102/156)
Buried 18 May 1689 St Martin, Coney Street (PReg)

Luty, George (Lewty, Lutey) *1636

Goldsmith, son of William Luty, blacksmith, Free by patrimony 1613 (SS102/62)
Search of his shop made by two wardens of London company, 8 August 1635. Parcels of plate were removed which, upon assay on 10 August, were found to be substandard. After melting down or defacing raw material returned to him upon a fine and a pledge not to offend again (LGC Minute Book Si/259–266)
Active in 1636 (YAJ29/108)
Buried 6 September 1644 St Martin, Coney Street (PReg)

Mady, John (Maddie) *1607

Servant of William Todd (q.v.), goldsmith, who paid 3s for his swearing an oath to the London company, 17 July 1573 (LGC Minute Book L/158-9)
Goldsmith, Free 1576 (SS102/17)

Maltby, Henry Donkin

Watchmaker, Free by order 1812 (Malden)
Commences business as a clock and watchmaker and jeweller, Colliergate (YG 8 April 1811)
Of Pavement, wanting an apprentice. 'A youth of respectable parents will be treated with on reasonable terms' (YH 13 July 1811)

Married Miss Pulleyn of York (YkCo 3 July 1817)
In addition he also sold tea and coffee (YG 17 February 1821)
Teadealer of Pavement (Dir 1823)
Pavement premises to let (YG 13 May 1826)
Wine and Spirit Merchant, 6 Coppergate (Dir 1830)
Death of wife, Ann, aged 43 (YG 10 April 1841)
Married Miss Clark of Easingwold (YG 27 August 1842)
Councillor, Monk Ward, died aged 56 (YG 20 May 1843
Father of Swann Maltby of [23] St Saviourgate, Wine and Spirit Merchant,
Free by patrimony 20 July 1846 (Malden)

Malton, John
Taken into partnership by Ambrose Beckwith (q.v.) at Tea Kettle and
Lamp, next to the Black Swan, Coney Street (YkCo 19 December 1749)
Jeweller and goldsmith, Free by order 1757 (Malden) on payment of £25,
1 December 1757 (YCA B44/34)
Elected Councillor (YkCo 7 October 1760)
His partnership with Ambrose Beckwith dissolved April 1761
(Gubbins/11)
Insured with Sun Fire Office 1762–87) (LGC letter 11 November 1997)
At the Tea Kettle and Lamp, next to the Black Swan, Coney Street (YkCo
23 August 1763)
Moved to premises formerly occupied by Thomas Watkinson, comb–maker
deceased, in Coney Street (YkCo 10 January 1764)
Son John Malton (q.v.), apprenticed to him 29 April 1766 (YCA D14/89)
Death (YCh 29 October 1773)
Death of widow aged 78 (YkCo 11 July 1786))

Malton, John
Son of John Malton (q.v.), jeweller and goldsmith, apprenticed to his
father, indenture 29 April 1766, 7 years (YCA D14/89)
Silversmith (YH 13 December 1794)

Malton, Thomas
Jeweller and goldsmith, Free by order 1757 (SS102/278)

Mandefield, Edwin

Watchmaker and jeweller 66 & 67 Goodramgate (Dir 1876, 1887, 1893, 1895)

Married Elizabeth Eliza Kitchen (YG 2 January 1869)

Agent for Star Life Assurance Society (Dir 1885)

Died 30 August 1903 aged 57 buried York Cemetery grave 19283 heart disease (YCReg)

Mangy, Arthur (Mangye, Manegey)

Goldsmith, son of Henry Mangy (q.v.), goldsmith (Free 1651), Free by patrimony 1681 (SS102/156)

For plating the York Minster vergers' silver rods £4 2s 6d, for tipping, gilding and engraving the horn of Ulph [after its return to the Minster by Henry, Lord Fairfax], £4 5s, 1673 (SS35/139)

Moved to Leeds by December 1690 when his daughter Mary was baptised in the parish church there (PReg)

Paid £60 11s by Borough Treasurer, Leeds for making the town mace weighing 193 ounces Troy, 3 November 1694 (RHS)

Goldsmith of Leeds, aged 68, to be executed at the Tyburn, Knavesmire, for counterfeiting coin of the realm, 30 March 1696 (Knipe/44)

Tried 1 August 1696, thrice reprieved and finally executed 2 October 1696, buried St Mary, Castlegate, on the same day (RHS & PReg)

Wife, Elizabeth, buried St Mary, Castlegate, 4 April 1698 (PReg)

Father of Arthur Mangy, Free by patrimony 1714 (SS102/206)

Father of Thomas Mangy, prebendary of Durham 1721–55

Mangy, Christopher (Mangie, Monigie, Mungie) *1615–45

Goldsmith, Free 1610 (SS102/58)

Chamberlain 1626 (SS102/75)

Father of George Mangy (q.v.), goldsmith, Free by patrimony 1639 (SS102/92)

Father of Henry Mangy (q.v.), goldsmith, Free by patrimony 1650/1 (SS102/110)

Mangy, Edward (Mangie)

Watchmaker, son of Edward Mangy, whitesmith, Free by patrimony 1659 (SS102/123)

Free of Hull by purchase 1660 (YAJ57/149)

Goldsmith of Church Lane October 1660 (YAJ60/118)

Aged 27, licence to marry Katherine Spalding at St Martin, Coney Street, 1661 (YASRS43/14)

Taxed on 5 hearths in Church Lane 1673 (YAJ60/118)

Died 1685 (YAJ57/156)

Widow, Katherine, died 1725 aged 88 (YAJ57/159)

Father of Edward Mangie, goldsmith of Hull, Free of Hull by patrimony 1695 (YAJ57/157)

Mangy, George (Mungie) *1660

Goldsmith, son of Christopher Mangy (q.v.), goldsmith (Free 1610), Free by patrimony 1639 (SS102/92)

Baptised 17 November 1619 St Martin, Coney Street, (PReg)

Chamberlain 1655 (SS102/115)

Father of Thomas Mangy (q.v.), goldsmith, Free by patrimony 1665 (SS102/130)

Wife, Frances, buried 18 February 1667 St Martin, Coney Street (PReg)

Mangy, George

Goldsmith, son of Henry Mangy (q.v.), goldsmith (Free 1651), Free by patrimony 1676 (SS102/148)

Mangy, Henry (Mungie)

Goldsmith, son of Christopher Mangy (q.v.), goldsmith (Free 1610) Free by patrimony 1651 (SS102/110)

Baptised 6 June 1626 St Martin, Coney Street (PReg)

Living in St Mary, Castlegate parish, September 1674 (RHS)

Father of George Mangy (q.v.), goldsmith, Free by patrimony 1676 (SS102/148)

Father of Arthur Mangy (q.v.), goldsmith, Free by patrimony 1681 (SS102/156)

Mangy, Thomas *1659–83

Goldsmith, son of George Mangy (q.v.). goldsmith (Free 1639), Free by patrimony 1665 (SS102/130)

Paid Hearth Tax on 5 hearths in a house in St Michael le Belfrey parish, 1671 (Hearth/8)

Six bodkins, six dram cups and beakers bought from him by Edward Malt on behalf of Major John Wallis who, on 17 May 1761, claimed expenses of £8 1s 1d from the wardens of the London company. These expenses included other items bought from Robert Williamson (q.v.) and Rowland Kirby (q.v.) as well as carriage and letters (LGC Court Book 6/196–7)

Chamberlain 1683 (SS102/157)

Mannering, William (Manrin)

Son of William Mannering of Dringhouses, innkeeper, apprenticed to William Astley (q.v.), goldsmith, indenture 10 July 1797, 7 years, consideration £26 10s (YCA D15/111)

His wife, Mary, died 1 November 1805, aged 61, convulsions, MI St Stephen's, Acomb (PReg)

Publican of Dringhouses, died 8 November 1805 aged 55, MI St Stephen's, Acomb (PReg)

Marle, John

Goldsmith, Free 1544 (SS96/264)

Marsh, Philemon *1654–66

Goldsmith, Free 1652 (SS102/112)

Married Mary Alexander of South Shields 15 June 1654 at South Shields (HM)

One hearth in house in St John del Pike parish demolished (Hearth/17)

Buried 25 April 1672 St Michael, Spurriergate (PReg)

Will 20 April proved 12 September 1672 (YASRS60/65)

Father of Richard Marsh, Free by patrimony 1693 (SS102/172), merchant, who was buried 1 June 1705 St Michael. Spurriergate (PReg)

Marshall, John

Apprentice to Robert Hutchinson (q.v.), goldsmith, who in his will, 12

March 1506, bequeathed all the tools in his shop to his 'friend and apprentice' (YWCWG)

Employed by Sir John Gilliot (q.v.) and legatee of his will, 28 December 1509 (YWCWG)

Marshall, Martha

Jeweller, 6 Coney Street (Dir 1818 & 1823)

Stock purchased by John Hardy (q.v.) (YG 8 May 1824)

Marshall, Roger

Goldsmith, son of John Marshall, (mercer, Free 1445) formerly Lord Mayor of York (1467 & 1480), Free by patrimony 1482 (SS96/204)

Marshall, Thomas

Goldsmith, Free 1489 (SS96/213)

Mascall, William *1671–73

Goldsmith, son of Thomas Mascall, embroiderer, Free by patrimony 1664 (SS102/130)

Son, Thomas, buried St Martin, Coney Street, 17 August 1672 (PReg)

Mason, Alex

Apprenticed to William Thornton (q.v.), clockmaker, indenture 16 August 1672, 6 years, consideration £30, tax of 15s paid 25 January 1763 (PRO)

Matthew

Goldsmith

Grantor of land in Newbiggin (Monkgate end of Lord Mayor's Walk) 1184x1200 (SRJ/634)

Wife, Alice, grantor of land in Bootham 1184x1200 (SRJ/608)

Son, Franche, grantor of land in Bootham 1184x1200 (SRJ/609)

Maud, Edmund (Mawde)

Goldsmith, son of John Maud, draper, Free by patrimony 1678 (SS102/152)

Father of John Maud, Free by patrimony 1698 (SS102/180)

Maye, Joseph

Son of Christopher Maye of Kingston upon Hull, yeoman, apprenticed to Henry Sprocke (q.v.), goldsmith, 7 years, 1 May 1597 (YCA D12/11b)

Mears, John

Toyman, Free by order 1826 (Malden)

Of W. & J. Mears, jewellers and hardwaremen, Pavement (Dir 1818)

Married Miss Renolds of York (YG 6 May 1820)

Jeweller of Pavement (YG 18 May 1822 & Dir 1823)

Of High Ousegate (YG 4 November 1826)

Jeweller, hardware and toyman, 8 High Ousegate (YG 23 May 1829 & Dir 1830)

Of 24 High Ousegate (YG 19 February 1831)

Mears, William

Hardwareman, Free by order 1816 (Malden)

Of W. & J. Mears, jewellers and hardwaremen, Pavement (Dir 1818)

Menseton, Thomas de

Goldsmith, Free 1389 (SS96/87)

Grantor of a tenement in Aldeconey Street [Lendal] 1401 (SRJ/1590)

Former proprietor of land in Davygate 1409 (SRJ/1591)

Millner, Thomas
Clockmaker, son of Thomas Millner, merchant tailor, Free by patrimony 1741 (SS102/259)
Clockmaker of Leather Lane, London, 1741 (Poll)

Milne, Charles (Millne)
Jeweller, son, George William, baptised 23 April 1837 Holy Trinity, Goodramgate (PReg)
Silversmith and jeweller of Acomb, died 10 March 1859 aged 53 buried York Cemetery grave 1161 paralysis (YCReg)

Monkton, Simon de
Goldsmith of York
Former proprietor of land in Footless Lane [Museum Street] 1352 (SRJ/1461), 1377 (SRJ/1462), 1387 (SRJ/1463)

Morley, Robert
Clockmaker, son of Nehemiah Morley, tanner, Free by patrimony 1733 (SS102/234)
Watchmaker of Ousebridge 1741 (Poll)

Morrett, John (Morritt)
Jeweller, son of John Morrett, butcher, Free by patrimony 1722 (SS102/219)
Jeweller of Ball and Mouth Street, London, 1741 (Poll)

Morton, Richard (Moreton)
Son of John Morton, Brazier, Free by patrimony as a brazier 1758 (SS102/285)
Brazier of Derby 1758, Silversmith of Sheffield 1784 (Poll)

Mower, Robert
Goldsmith, Free 1550 (SS96/271)

Mowrhouse, William
Goldsmith, Free 1557 (SS96/277)

Muchechaumpe, Simon de
Goldsmith, Free 1339 (SS96/33)

Munketon, Adoe,
Goldsmith, known in 1313 (Jackson/296)

Munkton, Roger de
Goldsmith, Free 1328 (SS96/24)
Workshop in Stonegate (Pedersen/8)
Witness at marriage of son, Simon, to Agnes Huntington at St Michael le Belfrey, 25 November 1341 (Pedersen/10)

Myers, Thomas
Parent–in–law George Cowley of York, glass grinder, apprenticed to Peter Goulett (q.v), jeweller, indenture 17 November 1757, 7 years (YCA D14/14)
Jeweller, bought large stock from London to commence business in York but died before he could do so (YkCo 3 January 1769)

Myers, Walter
Born 4 April 1917, apprentice steel engraver at the Ebor Press 1 February

1932, left 27 April 1946 to set up his own firm

Founded Cameo Engraving Co. in 1948 at 5A The Crescent (YEP 1 August 1981)

Maker's mark, WM, registered with Sheffield Assay Office 16 February 1970 (letter from librarian at Sheffield Assay Office)

Firm owned by Paul and Keith Myers (YEP 1 August 1981)

Firm owned by Paul and Judy Myers with premises at 5A The Crescent, 30 Holgate Road and 43 The Shambles (YEP 7 March 1994)

Mynskypp, Robert de

Goldsmith, Free 1369 (SS96/66)

Myrfyne, William

Finer at York Mint, witness to the will of Richard Ugdon, Master of the York Mint, 8 May 1545, who left 20s to the wife of cousin Myrfyn (SS106/226 & 227)

Nassing, John

Goldsmith, Free 1445 (SS96/163)

Neuby, Gerard de

Goldsmith, Free 1352 (SS96/46)

Neuby, William de

Goldsmith, paid rent for third shop on Ouse Bridge opposite the chapel, 16s, 25 January 1376 (SS120/7)

Of St Michael, Spurriergate, paid poll tax of 2s 8d with wife Isabella, 1381 (Bartlett/22)

? Free as a merchant, 1389 (SS96/87)

Neukirk, Michael de

Goldsmith of Flanders, Free 1348 (SS96/40)

Neuland, John (Newland)

Goldsmith, son of William Neuland, draper, Free by patrimony 1420 (SS96/129)

Former proprietor of land and tenements in Davygate 1435 (SRJ/4277 & 4278)

Witness to and, with daughter, Margaret, legatee of the will, 21 May 1440, of William Duke (q.v.), goldsmith (YWCWG)

Father of John Neuland, clerk [Rector of Wigginton c. 1453–64], Free by patrimony 1462 (SS96/182)

Administration of his estate granted 27 September 1465 (YASRS6/121)

Nevergelt, John

Goldsmith, Free 1432 (SS96/145)

Newbald, James

Baptised 20 August 1794, Holy Trinity, King's Court, son of James Newbald, deceased, late trumpeter Inniskilling Dragoons, and his wife, Marion, daughter of William Sturdy (PReg)

Married Mary Ann Whitworth 1817 South Muskham, Nottinghamshire (Loomes/130)

Working at Snaith 1820 (Loomes/130)

Watchmaker of the Shambles, three children, born to his wife, Mary Ann, baptised St Crux 1825–28 (PReg)

Watch and clockmaker, 12 Goodramgate (Dir 1830)
Died 29 January 1848 aged 53 at Ryther while on a visit there
(Loomes/130)

Newlove, John
Watchmaker of Foss Bridge (Dir 1818)
Of Pavement, four children, born to his wife, Ann, baptised St Crux
1819–28 (PReg)
Watch and clockmaker, 17 Pavement (Dir 1830, 1834)

Newsome, John
Locksmith, Free 1568 (SS102/10)
At the instigation of the inhabitants about Ousebridge, the Lord Mayor was
to request him to amend, repair and keep in order the clock on St
William's chapel, the council chamber, on Ouse Bridge, 27 April 1593
(YCA B31/10)
Kinsman of Bartholomew Newsam of London, clockmaker to Queen
Elizabeth (Dinsdale/68)
Father of George Newsome, vintner, Free by patrimony 1617 (SS102/67)

Newstead, Christopher
Son of George Newstead, joiner, Free by patrimony as a joiner 1755
(Malden)
Of the Mount, joiner and clockmaker, died aged 71 (YH 17 January 1801)

Newton, Henry Jones
Born Woodlesford, aged 26 in 1881 (Census 1881)
Married Louisa Kleiser (aged 47 in 1881), widow of Otmar Kleiser (q.v.),
3 February 1874 (YG 21 February 1874) when she transferred the business
to him (YAYAS34/7)
Watchmaker and Jeweller of 24 Parliament Street (Dir 1881, 1887 and
1889)

Newton alias Barbour, William
Goldsmith, son of Henry Newton alias Barbour, formerly one the mayor's
sergeants at mace, Free by patrimony 1495 (SS96/220)

Nicholas
Goldsmith, son of Ranulph (q.v.), goldsmith
Recipient of land in All Saints in the Marshes (Peasholme Green) parish
1244x1258 (SRJ/396 and 397) 1258x1296 (SRJ/394)
Grant to him by Thomas le Grant of land in Layerthorpe 1250x1299
(YASRS148/149)
Grant by him to John Raold, priest, of same land in Layerthorpe, August
1263 (YASRS148/149)
Grant to him by Hugh, son of Richard Cressi, of land in Layerthorpe,
1250x1299 (YASRS/148)

Nicholson, Valentine
Jeweller, son of Valentine Nicholson, gentleman, Free by patrimony 1734
(SS102/239)

Nicholson, William
Jeweller, son of Valentine Nicholson, attorney, Free by patrimony 1741
(SS102/259)

Norris, Richard

Son of Robert Norris, innholder of Beverley, apprenticed to Ambrose Beckwith I (q.v.), jeweller, indenture 21 March 1763, 7 years, consideration £40 (YCA D14/63)

Jeweller, Free 1770 (Malden)

Married Sally Corney (YkCo 27 March 1770)

Jeweller and goldsmith, started his own business at Golden Tea Kitchen, Coney Street (YkCo 8 May 1770)

Moves to house on corner of Spurriergate opposite Ousegate (YkCo 20 November 1770)

Bankrupt, stock for sale (YkCo 1 December 1772 & 2 March 1773)

Dividend of 5s 4d in the pound paid to his creditors (YkCo 7 June 1774)

North, Edward

Born 23 December 1822, baptised 5 January 1823 St Martin, Coney Street (PReg)

Jeweller, son of William North (q.v.), silversmith (Free 1816), Free by patrimony 31 October 1844 (Malden)

Married Mary, the eldest daughter of Jabez Punderson (YG 1 March 1845)

North, Lancelot

Clockmaker, son of William North, innholder, Free by patrimony 1624 (SS102/74)

Required to discharge a stranger whom he had hired as a clockmaker or alternatively pay a fine of 40s, 28 February 1626 (YCA B35/34b)

North, William *

Born 12 baptised 19 March 1795 All Saints, Pavement (PReg)

Silversmith, [second] son of William Graves North (q.v.), whitesmith, Free by patrimony [3 September] 1816 (Malden)

Married Ann Dove of York 23 March 1819 (RHS)

Silversmith of Feasegate 1818 & 1820 (Poll)

Partnership formed 1823 with George Dalby Cattle (q.v.), died 1838, and James Barber (q.v.), dissolved July 1847 (YG 24 July 1847)

Silversmith of South Parade 1830 (Poll)

Chamberlain 1832 (RHS)

Sheriff 1839/40 (RHS)

Father of Edward North (q.v.), jeweller, Free 31 October 1844 (Malden)

Silversmith, jeweller, watchmaker of 24 Coney Street (Dir 1849)

Died 13 June 1863 aged 68 of Heworth Green, buried York Cemetery grave 10225 ascites (YCReg)

North, William Graves

Baptised 12 March 1772 St Dennis (PReg)

Whitesmith, son of John North, whitesmith [of Fossgate], Free by patrimony [5 July] 1793 (Malden)

Of Feasegate, assay master for York Goldsmiths' Company for upwards of 30 years (Gubbins/5)

Chamberlain 1816 (RHS)

Father of William North (q.v.), silversmith, Free by patrimony 1816 (Malden)

Gentleman of The Cottage, Monk Bridge, 1830 (Poll)
Died 22 June 1838 aged 65 of Heworth Road buried York Cemetery grave 10226 apoplexy (YCReg)

Oliver, John *1684–90
Goldsmith, Free 1676 (SS102/148)
Buried 17 September 1696 St Michael le Belfrey (PReg)

Omere, William (Omerey)
Goldsmith, Free 1473 (SS96/193)
Debt of 4s 4d pending on chamberlains' accounts payable to John Fery, sergeant at mace, 3 February 1475. Increased to 4s 8d payable to William Lambe, sergeant at mace, 1 August 1476. Still pending, payable to Richard Burgges, sergeant at mace, 3 February 1476 but settled in full. Further debt of 40d payable to Richard Burgges, sergeant at mace, 3 February 1476 settled in full. (Attreed/12, 18, 91 & 92)

Orbatour, John le
Goldbeater of York, witness to documents 1317 (SRJ/3675), 1320 (SRJ/1485), 1323 (SRJ/1774 & 1788)

Orbatur, Walter le
Goldbeater of York, witness to a deed, 19 August 1272 (YCA B7/7b)
Holder of a toft in Monkgate, paid rent (husgabel) of 14d on it, 1284 (YAJ50/86)

Osbaldson, Thomas
Goldsmith, Free 1469 (SS96/188)
Concerned in a slander. He had heard Thomas Welles (q.v.) say that Herman Goldsmith (q.v.) was an 'untrewe man', 14 November 1476 (YCA B1/13b)

Overton, Thomas de
Goldsmith of York, witness to a document 1220x1280 (SRJ/1604)

Paddesley, John
Goldsmith, master of the Tower, Calais, York and Bristol mints 1434–45. Prime warden of the London company 1435, Died 1451 (Reddaway/300)

Palmer, William
Of York, 1715. Published *A Great Improvement in Watchwork directed to finding the Longitude* (Dinsdale/69)
Deadscape clock at York Minster made by Mr Palmer of York, before 1720 (Law/684)

Paraunt, John
Goldsmith, Free 1412 (SS96/116)

Parker, Edward
Goldsmith, silversmith, son of Edward Parker, merchant, Free by patrimony (occupation not stated) 1692 (SS102/171)
Father of Thomas Parker (q.v.), silversmith, Free by patrimony 1722 (SS102/220)
Known in 1733 (Jackson/299)
Father of William Parker, stay–maker, Free by patrimony 1734 (SS102/242)

Parker, John

Watchmaker of York, c.1650, watch in Webster collection (Dinsdale/69)

Parker, Thomas

Silversmith, son of Edward Parker (q.v.), silversmith, Free by patrimony 1722 (SS102/220)

Parker, Thomas

Working jeweller of Waterworth's Passage, Fossgate (Dir 1849)

Working jeweller, goldsmith, watch and clock maker, 16 Jubbergate (YG 3 May 1851)

Stock in trade to be sold by auction in consequence of severe indisposition (YG 6 March 1852)

Jeweller, house and shop on the corner of Petergate and Minster Yard for sale (YG 8 August 1854)

Parnell, George Thomas

Son of Ann Parnell of York, widow, apprenticed to Christopher Watson (q.v.), jeweller, indenture 4 October 1821, 7 years (YCA D16/82)

Jeweller, Free 1830 (Malden)

Working jeweller, 6 Little Blake Street (Dir 1830)

Paryssh, Agnes de

Widow of John de Paryssh (q.v.), goldsmith, tenure of indenture of Robert Russell (q.v.), his apprentice, left to her, 18 April 1393 (YWCWG)

Paryssh, John de (Parys, Parisch, Parysch)

Goldsmith, Free 1373 (SS96/71)

Will dated 18 April 1393, not proved, to be buried at St Helen, Stonegate. Left a silver spoon with a leopard knob and a gold ring with a lion. Executor and legatee wife Agnes. Legatee William Selar (q.v.), goldsmith (YASRS38/47, YWCWG)

Wife, Agnes, married Robert Russell (q.v.), goldsmith, her husband's apprentice (YASRS38/53)

Paulinus

The goldsmith

Witness to a grant, 1269 (YASRS148/151)

Witness to a deed, 19 August 1272 (YCA B7/7b)

Grant by his daughter, Mariota, of all her lands in Fossgate which she had had from her late mother, Ellen, to Jeremy Lorfeuer (q.v.) and Agnes, his wife, 1286/7 (BTC16/57)

Quitclaim by his son, Paulinus, to German (q.v.), the goldsmith, concerning all the lands and tenements in Fossgate which he and his wife, Ellen, had lately held and occupied, 1299 (BTC16/58)

Witness to a grant, 1316 (BTC16/60)

Peacock, William

Born a Quaker 28 March 1768 in the parish of St Sampson (YCA Freedom claim)

Watchmaker, son of Daniel Peacock, weaver and dyer, Free by patrimony [29 May] 1789 (Malden)

Came to York from the firm of Dwerrihouses, Berkeley Square, London (YH 17 March 1792)

Watchmaker, Spurriergate (Dir 1798, 1818 & 1823)

Chosen Councillor, Walmgate Ward (YCh 2 October 1817)

Chamberlain 1830 (RHS)

Gentleman, 11 Spurriergate (Dir 1830)

Revising Assessor of the City Commissioners, died aged 73 (YG 18 December 1841)

Pearson, George

Goldsmith, son of William Pearson (q.v.), goldsmith, Free by patrimony 1601 (SS102/45)

Wife, Isabell, buried 24 August 1604 St Martin, Coney Street (PReg)

Pearson, Peter *1608–22

Born 29 June 1585 (YASES3/345)

Goldsmith, son of William Pearson (q.v.), goldsmith, Free by patrimony 1604 (SS102/49)

Married Mary Tomlinson, 19 April 1607 St Mary, Bishophill Senior (PReg)

Father of Christopher Pearson, mariner, Free by patrimony 1634 (SS102/85)

Will 27 May 1632 proved 11 May 1635, Executor and legatee wife, Mary (YWCWG)

Pearson, William (Pereson)

Servant of George Kitchin (q.v.), goldsmith, who paid 3s for his swearing an oath to the London company, 17 July 1573 (LGC Minute Book L/158–9)

Goldsmith, Free 1574 (SS102/14)

For making the city's new mace and garnishing its two swords £25 8s 3d, 19 May 1580

For 55 ounces of silver and making and gilding the great mace	£24 0s 3d
For a bolt of iron for the mace, to the smith	4s 0d
For garnishing the two swords and for silver and gilding them	24s 0d
	(YCA B27/238b)

For mending the screws on the city's lesser mace 3s 4d, 13 October 1581 (YCA B28/30b)

Searcher, having abused himself towards the Lord Mayor to be committed in ward to Monk Bar during the Lord Mayor's pleasure, to be relieved the next day, 22 March 1582 (YCA B28/94b)

Award of arbitrators appointed to decide on disputes between George Kitchen and his fellow goldsmiths, Thomas Waddy (q.v.), William Pearson, John Stock (q.v.), John Raylton (q.v.) and Martin Byggyn (q.v.) 25 October 1583 (YCA B28/114)

Replaced as searcher 15 January 1583 (YCA B28/121)

For renewing 4 of the waits' badges, 7s, 1593 (YCA B31/27)

Father of George Pearson (q.v.), goldsmith, Free by patrimony 1600 (SS102/45)

Father of Peter Pearson (q.v.), goldsmith, Free by patrimony 1604

(SS102/49)

Pennock, John

Son of William Pennock of Guisbrough, gunsmith, apprenticed to William Kidson (q.v.), clockmaker, indenture 1 May 1617, 8 years, consideration food and clothing (YCA D12/40)

Moved to London and joined the Clockmakers company, Master 1660–63 (Loomes/137)

Perry, Robert

Silversmith, Paul, natural son by Elizabeth Rushton, born 16 May baptised 16 May 1779 St Crux (PReg)

Peter

The goldsmith

Grant to him by the prior of Marton of a toft in St Andrewgate, c.1252 (YASRS148/253)

Peters, Edward

Son of Mary Peters of York, widow, apprenticed to Christopher Watson (q.v.), jeweller, indenture 5 November 1814, 7 years (YCA D15/302)

Jeweller, Free 1826 (Malden)

Pigott, Richard

see Pygot, Richard

Pikeryng, Robert de (Pikkeryng)

Goldsmith, Free 1387 (SS96/85)

Will 26 proved 30 March 1403, to be buried St Michael, Spurriergate. Executor and legatee wife, Agnes (YASRS6/130, YWCWG)

Pierce, Samuel

Son of Thomas Pierce of Holywell, Flint, Wales, butcher, apprenticed to John Hampston, (q.v.), John Prince (q.v.), Robert Cattle (q.v.) and George Cattle (q.v.), jewellers and silversmiths, indenture 1 July 1796, 7 years (YCA D15/100)

Pinchbeck, John de

Goldsmith, Free 1376 (SS96/73)

Of St Helen, Stonegate, parish, paid 4d poll tax 1377 (YAJ43/138)

Of St Helen, Stonegate, parish, paid poll tax of 2s 0d with wife Alicia, 1381 (Bartlett/43)

Living with John Aug[ho]o (q.v.) and others in a tenement in Stonegate between the tenements of the prebends of Barneby and Bilton and extending in length from the high street to the tenement of the prebend of Masham 4 October 1392 (SS186/25)

Platt, Timothy

Apprenticed to Ambrose Beckwith II (q.v.), jeweller and goldsmith, indenture 26 September 1771, 7 years, consideration £25 (PRO)

Subject of a summons when his master was charged with deserting his pupil and leaving him unprovided for. The magistrates released him from his indenture, 1776 (Gubbins/12 and 56)

Plattes, Robert

Clockmaker, son of John Plattes, cook, Free by patrimony 1590 (SS102/33)

Plena, Henry de
Goldsmith, Free 1361 (SS96/55)

Plompton, Richard (Plumton, Plumpton)
Goldsmith and haberdasher, son of Robert Plompton, Common Clerk [town clerk], Free by patrimony 1505 (SS96/229)
Member of Corpus Christi Guild 1509 (SS57/170)
Died in Antwerp 1544, leaving a son John [Hauncie], then a minor (SS57/170)

Plumer, James (Plummer) *1627–52
Apprenticed to Christopher Harrington (q.v.), goldsmith, 7 years, 20 October 1613 (YCA D12/44)
Bequest of an 'amellinge Morter and pestell and a paire of amellinge tonges' to 'my mann' James Plummer, by Christopher Harrington (q.v.), goldsmith, 11 November 1614 (Rel/213)
Goldsmith, son of Michael Plumer, tailor, Free by patrimony 1620 (SS102/70)
Chamberlain 1628 (SS102/77)
Search of his shop made by two wardens of London company, 8 August 1635. Parcels of plate were removed which, upon assay on 10 August, were found to be substandard. After melting down or defacing raw material returned to him upon a fine and a pledge not to offend again (LGC Minute Book Si/259–266)
Required under the will of William Brearey, merchant, 16 January proved 16 February 1637, to make for his brothers and sisters, nine pieces of plate to the value of £3 of 'lawfull English money' to be inscribed 'The Guift of my brother Willm Brearey' and a further similar piece to be made for his cousin, Mary Secker, inscribed 'The Guift of my cosen Willm Brearey'. (BIHR Test Ebor Vol 42b fo 713)
One of the supervisors of the will of Thomas Harrington (q.v.), goldsmith, 11 December 1642 [the transcription says 'Johnnes Plumer, goldsmith,' but he was only 16 in 1642] (Rel/215)
Mended the little mace at York using 23 oz 4d of silver for which he was paid 16s 3d, 28 July 1648 (Jewitt/459)
Father of John Plumer (q.v.), goldsmith, Free by patrimony 1649 (SS102/108)
Father of Michael Plumer (q.v.), goldsmith, Free by patrimony 1659 (SS102/123)
Buried 3 June 1663 St Martin, Coney Street (PReg)

Plumer, John (Plomer) *1653–81
Goldsmith, baptised 5 March 1626, St Martin, Coney Street (PReg), son of James Plumer (q.v.), goldsmith (Free 1620), Free by patrimony 1649 (SS102/108)
Paid £4 10s for altering the arms of Charles I on the city mace, 25 March 1651 (YCA C24/15b)
Paid Hearth Tax on 3 hearths in a house in St Michael le Belfrey parish, 1671 (Hearth/7)
Paid £26 2s 6d in 1674/5 by Richmond Corporation 'for making the new

mace over and above the old mace'. He added a crown on the mace made during the Commonwealth by his father (Jewitt/479)

Wife, Magdalen, buried 3 January 1677 St Michael le Belfrey (PReg)

Buried 4 November 1680 St Michael le Belfrey (PReg)

Father of Timothy Plumer, Free by patrimony 1688 (SS102/165)

Plumer, Michael

Goldsmith, baptised 2 February 1631, St Martin, Coney Street (PReg), son of James Plumer (q.v.), goldsmith (Free 1620), Free by patrimony 1659 (SS102/123)

Known in 1689 (Jackson/298)

Plumer, Timothy (Plomer)

Goldsmith, baptised 20 May 1663, St Michael le Belfrey (PReg), son of John Plomer (q.v.), goldsmith (Free 1648), Free by patrimony 1688 (SS102/165)

Pollard, Hans

Jeweller, Free 1414 (SS96/119)

Pollard, William

Son of Thomas Pollard of York, shopkeeper, apprenticed to Richard Norris (q.v.), goldsmith, indenture 9 May 1770, 8 years, later assigned to Thomas Marshall, butter factor (YCA D14/122)

Goldsmith, Free 1780 (Malden)

Popilton, William de

Goldbeater, Free 1278 (SS96/3)

Porter, Peter

Goldsmith, Free 1390 SS96/89)

Porter, Walter

Goldsmith, Free 1396 (SS96/96)

Potts, John S.

Watch and clockmaker, 29 High Jubbergate (Dir 1858)

Potts, Joshua

Son of John Potts of Howden, watchmaker, apprenticed to John Hampston (q.v.), John Prince (q.v.), Robert Cattle (q.v.) and George Cattle (q.v.), jewellers and silversmiths, indenture 7 December 1802, 7 years (YCA D15/163)

Watchmaker, Free 1810 (Malden)

Married Hannah Atlay of Sheriff Hutton 22 December St Crux (PReg)

Maker of musical clocks (Dinsdale/70)

Watch and clockmaker took shop formerly occupied by W. Hornsey, linendraper, adjoining the White Swan in Goodramgate (YkCo 31 May 1815)

Watchmaker of Spurriergate 1818 (Poll)

Death of father aged 69, late of Patrington, at Hull (YCh 25 March 1819)

Of Spurriergate (YG 24 November 1821, 5 June 1830)

Death of wife, Hannah, aged 49 (YG 19 July 1845)

Watchmaker of 25 Spurriergate death by suicide, arsenic poisoning, 9 April 1854 aged 67 buried York Cemetery grave 6862 (YCReg & YG 15 April 1854)

Powell, Thomas
Jeweller, 3 Low Ousegate (Dir 1838)
Preston, Henry
Son of William and Elizabeth Preston of Easingwold, bricklayer (PReg)
Apprenticed to Henry Steward (q.v.), watchmaker, indenture 7 September
1829, 7 years, consideration £50 (YCA D6/236)
Watchmaker, Free 23 July 1838 (Malden)
Silversmith and jeweller of 8 Parliament Street 1844–1882 (YEP 16
January 1916)
One of original guarantors of Yorkshire Gala, 1858 (YEP 10 April 1916)
Director, York Gas Company 1877–1911 (YEP 16 January 1916)
Died 15 January 1917 aged 101 years 9 months 7 days buried York
Cemetery grave 1542 (YCReg)
Preston, William
Goldsmith, Free 1487 (SS96/212)
Pridgin, William
Son of Philip Pridgin of York, deceased, apprenticed to William Thornton
(q.v.), clockmaker, indenture 10 June 1756, 7 years (YCA D14/3)
Of Hull, Free 1778 (Malden)
Watchmaker, Colliergate 1784 (Poll)
Watchmaker, removed from Colliergate to Coney Street, opposite the
George Inn (YkCo 16 December 1788)
Possibly returned to Hull c.1793 (Walker/83)
Chosen as Common Councillor for Bootham Ward (YH 20 June 1795)
Prince, George
Goldsmith, known in 1636 (Jackson/298)
Prince, John * (Prence)
Son of John Prince of Skeldergate, bricklayer, apprenticed to Ambrose
Beckwith senior, goldsmith (YkCo 20 November 1770) baptised 30
October 1749 Holy Trinity, Micklegate (PReg)
Mrs Beckwith sold her husband's business in Coney Street to John
Hampston and John Prince, journeyman and apprentice respectively with
Ambrose Beckwith [senior] (YkCo 20 November 1770)

Jeweller, Free by patrimony 1771 (Malden)
Recommended, with William Clark(q.v.) and John Prince (q.v.), to repair
silver plate in the Mansion House, 25 February 1780 (YCA B45/12)
Married Sarah Nicholson of Cawood (YG 23 April 1782)
Chamberlain 1779 (RHS)

Elected as Councillor Micklegate Ward 1783 (RHS)

Refused office of Sheriff 1793, paid usual fine (YG 25 April 1835)

Lease of Scut Close, Fishergate (2 acres 2 roods 3 perches) conveyed to him for £350, 21/22 January 1794 (YCA Acc356)

With John Hampston (q.v.) built glass works on Scut Close 1797 (YEP 25 August 1983)

George Cattle (q.v.) and Robert Cattle (q.v.) joined the partnership c. 1796, Hampston, Prince and Cattles (HM)

Undivided moiety of glass manufactory, offices and dwelling house for workmen conveyed to John Hampston (died 26 January 1805) for £56 7s 6d, 5/6 June 1804 (YCA Acc356)

Retired from Prince and Cattles, Jewellers, 1807 (Gubbins/74)

Glass house and ground, Fishergate released to Henry Prest (died 1824), 1819 (YCA Acc356)

Glass business leased for one year to Charles Priestley, 1829 (YCA Acc356)

Wife, Sarah, died aged 73 (YG 8 July 1826)

Died aged 86 at 21 Fishergate after four year's illness (YG 25 April 1835)

Prince, Philip

Goldsmith of York

Married 27 August 1663 Eryholme Anne (baptised there 19 May 1635), eldest daughter of John Calverley of Eryholme. She died without issue 1 March 1667 and was buried in York Minster (Foster)

Prince, William

Goldsmith, Free 1646 (SS102/102)

Father of William Prince, Free by patrimony 1685 (SS102/160)

Pudsay, Christopher

Goldsmith, son of William Pudsay (q.v.), goldsmith (Free 1438), Free by patrimony 1472 (SS96/192)

Pudsay, John (Pudessay)

Goldsmith, Free 1438 (SS96/153)

Member of Corpus Christi Guild 1440 (SS57/38)

Bequeathed some tools by will of John Luneburgh (q.v.), goldsmith, 13 August 1458 (SS30/213)

Probate granted (no will existing) 30 October 1458 (YASRS6/133)

Pudsay, William

Goldsmith, Free 1438 (SS96/153)

Father of Christopher Pudsay (q.v.), goldsmith, Free by patrimony 1472 (SS96/192)

Pulleyn, Ralph (Pullan, Pullane)

Baptised Fewston (Pullein/180)

Goldsmith, Free 1502 (SS96/226)

Member, with wife, Alice, of Corpus Christi Guild 1506 (SS57/163)

For making two new pitchers for the high altar, repairing a holy water vase, for silver and gold, and for making and repairing some jewel boxes in York Minster, £4 9s, 1518/19 (SS35/99)

Chamberlain 1521 (SS96/242)

Paid 10s for an ounce of silver and gilding the long sword carried before the Lord Mayor, 1521/2 (Jewitt/451)

Witness to documents 1522 (SRJ/2506, 2507 & 2508)

Half a messuage and two and a half acres in Bramley Park surrendered to him and Thomas Pulleyn of Thackray by John Pulleyn of Lanehead House for nine years, 4 June 1522 (Pullein/181)

Of Bootham, St Michael le Belfrey parish, paid lay subsidy of 9s on goods of £18 and first levy of £8 on lands, 1524 (YAJ4/171)

Sheriff 1526/7 (Drake/364)

Alderman October 1528, discharged 24 July 1533, restored 6 June 1534 (RHS)

For repairing jewel boxes in York Minster for the last two years, 42s, 1531/2 (SS35/107)

Lord Mayor 1537 (Drake/364)

Doubt that his goods were worth £138 as assessed, 1540 (Palliser/141)

Will 11 February 1539 proved 5 March 1540, to be buried in St Thomas' choir in St Michael le Belfrey (YASRS11/139, YWCWG) His house in Stonegate as well as a house in North Street bequeathed to his wife, Alice, executor of the will. Daughter Ann, was wife of William Sides (Pullein/181)

Father of Anthony Pulleyn, merchant, Free by patrimony 1544 (SS96/264) Anthony Pulleyn and Alice, widow of Ralph Pulleyn, surrendered the fourth part of a messuage in Timble, once held by Ralph (Pullein/181)

Pygot, Richard (Pigott)

Goldfiner, Free 1534 (SS96/253)

Will 13 June proved 30 August 1538, to be buried near his children at St Wilfrid. Executor and legatee wife, Jane. Supervisor of will Alderman George Gale (q.v.) (YASRS11/136, YWCWG)

Pynder, Thomas

Goldsmith, son of William Pynder, tapiter, Free by patrimony 1587 (SS102/30)

Ralets, John

Apprentice to Robert Bekwith (q.v.), goldsmith, who paid 3s for his swearing an oath to the London company, 17 July 1573 (LGC Minute Book L/158–9)

Ralph, (Radulph)

Goldsmith, witness to a document 1214x1216 (SRJ/1718), witness to a grant 1200x1250 (YASRS148/77)

Grant by his son, Nicholas, to the Dean and Chapter of York of rental from land in the Marsh [Hungate area] 1225x1275 (YASRS148/156)

Ranulf

Goldsmith, witness to documents 1150x1200 (SRJ/1883), 1150x1210 (SRJ/1719), 1175x1250 (SRJ/1713)

Ranulph

Goldsmith, in possession of land in Gillygate 1220x1280 (SRJ/1603/4/5)

Tenant of land in the Marshes [Peasholme Green] 1261x1265 (SRJ/971)

Father of Nicholas (q.v.), goldsmith

Rawnson, William (Rawneson) *1583–1600
Goldsmith, flourished 1562 to 1593 (Jackson/298)
Legatee, with his wife, of the will, 19 April 1576, of Thomas Hutton
(q.v.), goldsmith (YWCWG)
For old silver for the Minster glazier to gilt with, 5d, 1577/8 (SS35/116)
For making for York Minster a new silver bowl on an old silver bowl 20s
8d, for mending 3 silver pots, 3s, 1579 (SS35/137)

Raylton, John (Rainton)
Goldsmith, Free 1575 (SS102/15)
Award of arbitrators appointed to decide on disputes between George
Kitchen and his fellow goldsmiths, Thomas Waddy (q.v.), William Pearson
(q.v.), John Stock (q.v.), John Raylton and Martin Byggyn (q.v.) 25
October 1583 (YCA B28/114)
Father of William Rainton, bricklayer, Free by patrimony 1624 (SS102/73)

Rayns, William (Raynes)
Free by order (no trade given) 1688 (SS102/164)
Clockmaker of York. While returning home from Helmsley, where his
brother, Thomas Rayns (Lord Mayor of York 1688), lived, he fell off his
horse two miles from Gilling and died there in January 1694 (Gilling
PReg)

Rayson, Henry John
Fancy repository and toy warehouse, 36 Parliament Street (Dir 1843)
Jeweller of 36 Parliament Street (Dir 1846)
Painter and dealer in toys, 36 Parliament Street (Dir 1851)
Fancy Repository, 32 Parliament Street (Dir 1857 & 1861)
Jeweller, 32 Parliament Street (Dir 1858)
Death of wife, Sarah, aged 78, 13 December 1885 (YG 19 December
1885)
Of 2 Fountayne Street (his daughter's house), painter, died 2 June 1888
aged 81 buried York Cemetery grave 2323 natural decay (YCReg)

Reed, Clement (Read) *1692
Known in 1695 (Jackson/299)
Goldsmith, Free 1699 (SS102/181)
A Mr Read appeared before Mr Loftus of the London company for selling
substandard gold and silver wares. He was ordered to pay 10s 6d, the costs
of the goods, and charges of 2s 0d, 23 August 1700 (LGC Court Book
10/220)

Reed, Thomas
Goldsmith, Free 1694 (SS102/172)

Reeve(s), Robert
Watchmaker, Free 1661 (SS102/124)
Married Elizabeth Adamson 1666 (Loomes/147)

Reginald
The goldsmith, witness to a grant 1270 (BTC16/91)

Regnolds, George (Renhoulds)
Watchmaker, Free 1642 (SS102/96)
Buried 4 April 1680 St Martin, Coney Street (PReg)

Renton, James
Son–in–law of George Hick of Apperley Bridge, innkeeper and farmer, apprenticed to Matthew Hick [his uncle] (q.v.), watchmaker, indenture 22 March 1831, 7 years, no consideration (YCA D16/285)
Clock and watchmaker and jeweller, took over a business at 42 Stonegate (YG 18 June 1836)
Moves to shop formerly occupied by Matthew Hick at Minstergates (YG 26 November 1836
Married Margaret, eldest daughter of R. Tranmer of Easingwold (YG 31 December 1836)
Watchmaker and Jeweller, South Entrance [Minstergates] (Dir 1838)

Rhoades, Charles (Rhodes) *1675–1707
Goldsmith, [third] son of Francis Rhoades, upholsterer, Free by patrimony 1677 (SS102/150)
Married Mary, daughter of Alderman William Raper, 27 August 1691 St Crux (PReg)
Chamberlain 1692 (SS102/170)
Sheriff 1694/5 (Drake/367)
Various children baptised at Holy Trinity, King's Court between 1698 and 1706 (PReg)
Country house at Murton in Osbaldwick parish (RHS)
Buried 19 June 1715 Holy Trinity, King's Court (PReg)
Will 8 February 1714 codicil 19 April proved 4 July 1715 (RHS)
Father of Gertrude Rhodes (baptised 13 June 1704, Holy Trinity, King's Court) milliner, Free by patrimony 1750 (SS102/270)

Rhoades, Mary (Rhodes)
Continued the business of her husband, Charles Rhoades (q.v.), goldsmith after his death in 1715.
Appeared before the court of the London company for selling gold and silver wares worse than standard. Fined £9 15s 6d which included the cost of the goods, 7 April 1720 (LGC Court Book 12/41)
Married, second, Wilfrid Tolson (q.v.) of St Martin, Coney Street, 28 August 1726 Holy Trinity, King's Court (PReg)
Reverted to the name of Rho[a]des after the death of her second husband in February 1732.
Insured with Sun Fire Office 1733 (LGC letter 11 November 1997)
Buried 22 December 1742 (as Mrs Mary Rhodes) Holy Trinity, King's Court (PReg)

Richardson, William
Goldsmith, Free 1517 (SS96/239)
Of Bootham, St Michael le Belfrey parish, paid lay subsidy of 2s 6d on goods of £5, 1524 (YAS4/170)
Paid lay subsidy of 4d on profits on wages of 20s 0d, 1524 (YAS4/177)
Father of Martin Richardson, painter, Free by patrimony 1555 (SS96/275)

Richmond, Joseph
Clockmaker, Free by order 1810 (Malden)
Clockmaker of Fossgate aged 61 buried 27 May 1818 St Crux (PReg)

Riley, Thomas
Son of John Riley of York, tailor, apprenticed to Edward Jackson (q.v.), jeweller and silversmith, indenture 9 August 1821, 7 years (YCA D16/97)
Robert
Goldsmith, joint confirmee of a grant of land in Patrickpool 1150x1200 (SRJ/1885)
Robert
The goldsmith, witness to a document 1292 (SRJ/665), witness to a grant 23 September 1295 (YASRS148/235)
Of St Martin, Coney Street parish, paid 2s 1d poll tax 1334 (YkHist13/8)
Witness to a grant 1337 (SRJ/19 & 2602)
Roberts, Samuel, junior
Plater and silversmith of Eyre Street Sheffield, in partnership with George Cadman (q.v.) and George Ingall as Roberts, Cadman & Co. Maker's marks registered at Sheffield 1785 and 1786. Assay at York 2 June 1809 (YAJ49/121)
Robinson, John
Goldsmith, son of Anthony Robinson, joiner, apprentice to Robert Casse[n] (q.v.), Free 1627 (SS102/77)
Rode, John
Goldsmith, Free 1421 (SS96/130)
Of Stonegate, will 27 September proved 10 October 1469, to be buried in the churchyard of St Michael le Belfrey next to his first wife, Agnes, Executor and legatee second wife, Johanna. Legatees John Andrew (q.v.), and John Colayne (q.v.), goldsmiths (YASRS38/52, YWCWG)
Roderham, Thomas
Appointed controller, changer and assayer of King's money within the castle of York, 16 July 1423 (CRP 1 Henry VI part v p131 – Cooper/153)
Roderham, William
See Rotherham, William
Rodes, Thomas
Goldsmith, Free 1430 (SS96/143)
Ronchetti, Peter Joseph
Witness at the marriage of Joseph Fattorini (q.v.) St Mary, Castlegate 30 January 1837 (PReg)
Jeweller and toyman, King's Square, premises for sale (YG 17 October 1840)
Married Miss Mary Ann Gee of Knaresborough (YG 15 January 1842)
Jeweller, 11 Parliament Street (YG 8 August 1846, Dir 1846 & 1850)
Mary Ann Ronchetti, fancy repository, 27 St Nicholas Street, Scarborough (Dir 1858)
Watchmaker, 10 Low Ousegate and 11 Parliament Street (Dir 1861)
Died 18 August 1878 at Scarborough aged 69 buried York Cemetery grave 14204 effusion on the brain (YCReg)
Widow, Mary Ann, died at Scarborough aged 69 (YG 22 December 1883)
Roodis, Peter
Goldsmith, member of Corpus Christi Guild 1422/3 (SS57/22)

Rooksby, John
Watchmaker, son of Miles Rooksby, baker, Free by patrimony 1648 (SS102/105)
Later of Hull (Walker/84)
Rosenberg, Harris
Jeweller, Free by order 1832 (Malden)
Giving up business, stock for sale (YG 25 February, 1 March 1837)
Jeweller, St Helen's Square (Dir 1838)
Furrier from 29 Red Cross Street, London and 104 Union Street Aberdeen, returned to York (YG 18 December 1841)
At Mr C. Richardson's shop, 27 Coney Street (YG 8 January 1842)
Roston, Roger de (Reston, Royston)
Goldsmith, Free 1305 (SS96/10)
MP for York 30 May 1306 (RHS & Park/40)
Bailiff 1307/8 (Drake/360)
With wife, Dionisia, founded chantry of St James in Holy Trinity, King's Court, 1320 (Drake/320)
Rotheram, William (Roderham)
Goldsmith, Free 1444 (SS96/162)
Will 2 August proved 11 August 1467, to be buried next to the tomb, of Richard Garton, brother–in–law, in St Michael le Belfrey. Executor and legatee wife, Cecile. Witnesses to will John Andrew (q.v.) and John Tirell (q.v.), goldsmiths (YASRS38/52, YWCWG)
Rousby, John
Watchmaker, son Jacob Rousby, Free by patrimony 1684 (SS102/159)
Rowen, Mr
Of York. Appeared before Mr Loftus of the London company for selling substandard gold and silver wares. Ordered to pay £2 8s, the costs of the goods, and charges of £2 16s 6d, 23 August 1700 (LGC Court Book 10/220)
Rowntree, Robert (Rawntree, Rountree)
Clock and watchmaker of Coppergate (Dir 1818 & 1823)
Matilda, daughter of Robert Rowntree and his wife, Hannah, baptised 22 November 1822 (PReg St Mary, Castlegate)
Of 124 Walmgate (1830 Dir) 109 Walmgate (Dir 1834)
Death (YG 1 August 1835)
Ruddock, Richard Martin
Son of Mary Ruddock of York, widow, apprenticed to John Harrison (q.v.), goldsmith and jeweller, indenture 1 January 1833, 7 years (YCA D16/318)
Living with Edward Jackson (q.v.), jeweller, Coney Street (1841 Census)
Rule, James
Watchmaker, becomes a dentist, in premises of W. Clark (q.v.), in Low Ousegate (YkCo 10 May 1785)
Assigns his effects (YkCo 4 February 1793)
Watchmaker, Ouse Bridge (Dir 1798) Low Ousegate (Dir 1806) Spurriergate (Dir 1809–11)

Death aged 58 (YkCo 4 March 1811)

Russe, William

Citizen and jeweller of London, master of King's Mints of the Tower, Calais, York and Bristol, 1431–34. Died 1534 (Reddaway/304)

Russell, Robert

Apprenticed to John de Paryssh (q.v.), goldsmith. His indentures transferred to Agnes de Paryssh (q.v.) on the death of her husband, John, in 1393 (YWCWG)

Goldsmith, Free 1395 (SS96/95)

Wife, Agnes, will 13 August 1396, not proved, to be buried at St Helen, Stonegate, near to John Parysh (q.v.), goldsmith, her first husband, (YASRS38/53)

Rykward, Nicholas

Goldfiner, Free 1565 (SS102/6)

Rylah, John

Son of George Rylah of York, apprenticed to William Whitwell (q.v.) and James Barber (q.v.), jewellers, indenture 28 February 1818, 7 years (YCA D16/20)

Rypplay, John

Clockmaker, repaired York minster clock 1453 (Loomes/149)

Clockmaker, son of John, chaplain, Free by patrimony 1472 (SS96/192)

Samuel, David

Of York, yeoman, apprenticed to George Hoy (q.v.), watchmaker, indenture 6 December 1809, 7 years, no consideration (YCA D15/237)

Watchmaker, Free 1820 (Malden)

Watchmaker of Hungate 1830 (Poll)

Sampson, William

Goldsmith, Free 1388 (SS96/86)

Of Bootham, St Michael le Belfrey parish, paid poll tax of 2s 0d with wife Emma, 1381 (Bartlett/52)

Sauvage, John (Savage)

Of St Saviour parish, paid poll tax with wife Agnes, 1381 (Bartlett/66)

Father of William Sauvage, sergeant, Free by patrimony 1427 (SS96/140)

Savage, James

Son of James Savage of Howden, yeoman, apprenticed to William Thornton (q.v.), clockmaker, indenture 2 February 1756, 7 years (YCA D13/125b)

Sawhell, George

Goldsmith, son of John Sawhell, minstrel, Free by patrimony 1556 (SS96/277)

Fined 5s by the two wardens of the London company during their searches in the north, 5 February 1561 (LGC minute book K/176)

Sawhell, Miles (Sawgheld)

Goldsmith, son of John Sawhell, minstrel, Free by patrimony 1551 (SS96/271)

Administration of estate granted 11 September 1564 (YASRS38/54)

Scardeburge, John de
Goldsmith, Free 1348 (SS96/40)
Of St Helen, Stonegate, parish, with wife paid 8d poll tax 1377 (YAJ43/139)
Of St Martin, Coney Street, parish, with wife and one servant paid 12d poll tax 1377 (YAJ43/137)
Scauceby, William
Goldsmith, Free 1415 (SS96/122)
Schwerer, Matthew
German clockmaker working in Hull 1790, 22 Sewer Lane 1813–4, 27 Mytongate 1818–32, 21 Mytongate 1834 (Walker/86) [possibly father of the Matthew referred to in the rest of this entry]
Watchmaker, jeweller and silversmith, in business with his brother, Phillip Schwerer (q.v.), in Petergate until 1842 when they returned to Germany. Re–commenced business on his own at 6 Stonegate, made complaint against Andrew Kleiser (q.v.) who was trading as P. Schwerer (YG 30 May 1846)
Watch and clockmaker, 18 Stonegate (Dir 1849)
Watchmaker, jeweller and silversmith, 14 Stonegate (Dir 1858)
Schwerer, Phillip
Clock and watchmaker maker commenced business, with his brother, Matthew Schwerer (q.v.), in Petergate (YG 23 September 1837)
Watchmaker, 99 Petergate (Dir 1838)
Business transferred to 38 Stonegate, autumn 1839 (YAYAS34)
Clockmaker , aged 35, employed Augustine Kleiser (q.v.) and Andrew Kleiser (q.v.) (Census 1841)
Returned to Germany in 1842. Business sold to Andrew Kleiser and Augustine Kleiser who continued to trade as P. Schwerer (YG 30 May 1846)
Seagrave, Edward
Baptised 7 April 1751 All Saints, Pavement (PReg)
Son of Edward Seagrave, brazier (deceased by 1776), apprenticed to Ambrose Beckwith senior (q.v.), jeweller, indenture 19 February 1767, 7 years, consideration £25 (PRO)
Jeweller, Free by patrimony [28 November] 1776 (Malden)
Jeweller of Peter Lane 1784 (Poll)
Seamer, Abell (Seamour)
Son of William Seamer (q.v.), watchmaker, apprenticed to his father, William Seamer (q.v.), clockmaker indenture 3 June 1629, 7 years (YCA D12/64b)
Watchmaker, Free by patrimony 1649 (SS102/108)
Died 1682 will dated 15 March 1677, legatees wife, Dorcas, daughters Dorcas and Hannah, sons Abell and Joseph (Loomes/157)
Father of Joseph Seamer, Free by patrimony 1714 (SS102/210)
Seamer, Joseph (Seamour, Seymour)
Son of William Seamer (q.v.), clock and watchmaker, apprenticed to his father, clockmaker and mother, Dorothy, indenture 8 June 1635, 7 years

(YCA D12/74)

Watchmaker, Free by patrimony 1649 (SS102/108)

Seamer, Peter

Son of William Seamer (q.v.), clock and watchmaker, apprenticed to his father, indenture 20 May 1628, 7 years, (YCA D12/64b)

Seamer, William (Seamor, Seymour)

Watchmaker, Free 1628 (SS102/77)

Wife, Dorothea (YCA D12/82)

Father of Peter Seamer (q.v.)

Father of Abell Seamer (q.v.), watchmaker, Free by patrimony 1649 (SS102/108)

Father of Joseph Seamer (q.v.), watchmaker, Free by patrimony 1649 (SS102/108)

Segar, John

Goldsmith, also called Hanse, Free 1415 (SS96/122)

Selander, Henry

Goldsmith, Free 1392 (SS96/91)

Selar, William

Of Bootham, St Michael le Belfrey parish, paid poll tax of 3s 0d with wife, Dulcia, 1381 (Bartlett/51)

Legatee of the will, 18 April 1393, of John de Paryssh (q.v.), goldsmith (YWCWG)

Will 18 January 1401 proved 28 June 1402, to be buried in the tomb of his first wife in St Michael le Belfrey. Executor and legatee second wife, Agnes. Legatee William Hovingham (q.v.), goldsmith. Property in Stonegate bequeathed to William and Hugh, sons of Wermbolti [de Harlam] (q.v.), goldsmith (YASRS6/147, YWCWG, SRJ/4049 & 4050/1)

Selby, John de

Goldsmith of York

Grant of 2 messuages, a dovecote and 5 acres of land at Holtby to him and William de Hessill, 24 May 1368 (YAJ17/102)

Seler, Hugh le

Goldsmith

Made, at York, a new seal for the bishopric of Durham [accession of Robert de Bury], 1333 (Cherry/57)

Seman, Bartholomew

see Goldbeater, Bartholomew

Sharpe, William

Goldsmith, son of John Sharpe, tailor, Free by patrimony 1632 (SS102/82)

Share, John (Sharr, Sharre)

Servant of William Todd (q.v.), goldsmith, who paid 3s for his swearing an oath to the London company, 17 July 1573 (LGC Minute Book L/158–9)

Goldsmith, Free 1591 (SS102/33)

Committed to ward for buying moulten silver from an unknown person. Released from his punishment to find the said person and bring him before the Lord Mayor on 10 November, 4 November 1596 (YCA B31/228)

Father of William Sharr, glover, Free by patrimony 1620 (SS102/70)

Sharpe, John

Watchmaker, 55 Fossgate (Dir 1867)

Died 9 October 1895 aged 61 buried York Cemetery grave 16845 consumption of the throat (YCReg)

Shockie, James le

A Frenchman, journeyman of George Kitchin (q.v.), goldsmith, who paid 3s for his swearing an oath to the London company, 17 July 1573 (LGC Minute Book L/158–9)

Shyngwell, John

Goldsmith, Free 1464 (SS96/183)

Skelton, Henry William

Son of William Skelton of York, apprenticed to William Darling (q.v.), watchmaker, indenture 1 January 1852, 7 years (D16/490)

Skelton, John

Goldsmith, son of Stephen Skelton, cook, Free by patrimony 1561 (SS102/3)

Skelton, Thomas

Goldsmith, known in 1450 (Jackson/297)

Sold mazers in the middle of the 15th century (Cripps/75)

Skelton, William

Silversmith & jeweller 25 Davygate (Dir 1834)

Working jeweller of 38 Stonegate (Dir 1838)

of 10 Feasegate (Dir 1843)

of 1 Feasegate (Dir 1846, 1849 & 1861)

Working jeweller and watchmaker of 1 Feasegate (Dir 1867)

Died 27 September 1874 aged 62 buried York Cemetery grave 17722 disease of the lungs (YCReg)

Skyres, William

Goldsmith, Free 1399 (SS96/102)

Searcher 5 March 1410 (SS120/75)

Confirmation of an assignment by Margaret Skyres, his widow, to John Mylner and Alice, his wife, of two houses on Ouse Bridge with two rooms above them and another room over the stallage of the bridge called Salmonhole, rent 40s a year. Skyres had leased these houses from the corporation in 1414 for 20 years and an additional 8 years was granted to the new tenants, 31 October 1424 (SS186/63)

Simson, Simpson

See Symson

Slyngesby, Nicholas

Goldsmith, Free 1408 (SS96/111)

Smeaton, John

Watchmaker, Free 1647 (SS102/104)

Chamberlain 1665 (SS102/130)

Great–grandfather of John Smeaton the eminent civil engineer. Died 25 August 1686 aged 62 at Austhorpe buried at Whitkirk MI (Thoresby2/73)

Will dated 16 August 1686 (Loomes/162)

Smith, David

Son of Charles Smith, cordwainer, apprenticed to Robert Cattle (q.v.) and James Barber (q.v.), jewellers, indenture 5 November 1808, 7 years (YCA D15/225)

Silversmith, Free 1818 (Malden)

Silversmith of Ogleforth 1818, of Stonegate 1830 (Poll)

Silversmith of Jubbergate, died 17 June 1840 aged 45 buried York Cemetery grave 2384 suicide by cutting his throat (YCReg)

Smith, Henry

Goldsmith, father of John Smith (Free by patrimony 1488) (SS96/213)

Smith, Henry

Son of John Smith (q.v.), watchmaker, apprenticed to his father, indenture 2 January 1752, 7 years (YCA D13/112b)

Smith, Horatio

Son of David Smith of Castle Howard, yeoman, apprenticed to William Fryer (q.v.), clock and watchmaker, indenture 27 January 1815, 7 years, consideration £29 (YCA D15/293)

Watchmaker, Free 1822

Clock and watchmaker, late assistant to Mrs Fryer, commenced business in Stonegate (YG 15 March 1823)

Married Sarah, 3rd daughter of T. Hall, collector of excise (YG 16 August 1823)

Watchmaker, silversmith and jeweller moved to shop in [57] Stonegate, formerly occupied by William Cattell (q.v.) (YG 30 July 1825)

Watchmaker of 7 Wilson's Terrace (Dir 1851)

Silversmith of Heworth died 6 May 1887 aged 88 buried York Cemetery grave 1906 old age (YCReg)

Smith, James

Apprenticed to Henry Hindley (q.v.), clockmaker, (but *cf* John Smith), belonged to the Newcastle company of comedians, died in the workhouse in Marygate aged 86, 1822 (Setchell/50)

Smith, John *1683–94

Goldsmith, son of William Smith, merchant tailor, Free by patrimony 1680 (SS102/153)

Chamberlain 1694 (SS102/172)

Sheriff 4 Dec 1698 (RHS & Drake/367)

Appeared before Robert Cuthbert of the London company for selling gold and silver wares worse than the standard. He was ordered to pay £5 6s, the costs of the goods, and a fine of £16 1s, 10 Feb 1700 (LGC Court Book 10/231)

Will 20 December 1705 proved 28 April 1712 (RHS)

Smith, John

Clockmaker, bonded as a papist, not to move more than 5 miles from his residence without a licence, 11 October 1745 (Aveling/272)

Watchmaker, Stonegate, had served his apprenticeship with Henry Hindley (YkCo 7 November 1749)

Clockmaker, Free by order 1751 (SS102/271)

Paid £30 for overhauling and renovating the clock at St Martin, Coney Street, 1754 (YG 18 December 1909)

Father of John Smith (q.v.), who was apprenticed to him 18 April 1758 (YCA D14/17)

Imprisoned in the Kidcote, required to deliver to the court a schedule of his estates and effects for the benefit of his creditors, suit executed by Thomas Thompson (YkCo 15 September 1761)

Tools for sale (YkCo 9 February 1762)

Papist, aged 51, for 9 years resident in St Martin, Coney Street, parish with wife, C——, and son, John, 1767 (Aveling/282)

Smith, John

Apprenticed to his father, John Smith (q.v.), clockmaker, indenture 18 April 1758, 7 years (YCA D14/17)

Papist, aged 23, 9 years resident in St Martin, Coney Street, 1767 (Aveling/282)

Married Cristan Tendelen of All Saints, Pavement, 6 February 1769 at St Martin, Coney Street (PReg)

Of Thirsk 1776–1807 (Dinsdale/76)

Smith, John

Son of William Smith of York, stonemason, apprenticed to Christopher Watson (q.v.), jeweller, 7 years, 19 April 1830 (YCA D16/261)

Smith, Robert (Smyth)

Goldsmith, Free 1564 (SS102/6), born Byland (YAJ57/122)

Smith, Timothy

Goldsmith, son of William Smith, tailor, Free by patrimony 1674 (SS102/146)

Died 1679 (Jackson/298)

Snawshill, William (Snaweshill, Snawsell)

Goldsmith, Free 1417 (SS96/125)

Father of William Snawsell (q.v.), goldsmith, Free by patrimony 1437 (SS96/152)

Will 7 May proved 25 May 1437 to be buried in the chapel of St Thomas the Martyr at St Michael le Belfrey. Executor and legatee wife, Margaret (YASRS38/57, YWCWG)

Snawshill, William (Snasell, Snawsdale, Snawsell, Snawesell, Snaweshill)

Goldsmith, [younger] son of William Snawshill (q.v.), goldsmith, Free by patrimony 1437 (SS96/152)

Married Joan (Jennet), daughter of John Thweng of Heworth (RHS)

Member, with his wife, of Corpus Christi Guild 1455 (SS57/57)

Gift of 18s to York Minster to build a new shop near the door of the cathedral, 1457 (SS35/68)

Witness to grants 23 & 26 February 1458 (YASRS148/128)

Chamberlain 1459 (SS96/178)

Admitted, with wife, Joan, member of Mercers' Guild 1464 (Cartulary/2b)

Granted, with others, land in Huntington and Clifton belonging to Robert Sharpils of Kingston upon Hull, 7 June 1464, confirmed 13 May 1467 (SS125/233)

Sheriff 1464/5 (Drake/363)

Witness to a grant 12 March 1465 (YASRS148/55)

Witness to and, with wife, Johanna, legatee of the will, 6 April 1466, of William Heend (q.v.), goldsmith (YWCWG)

Lord Mayor 1468 (Drake/363)

Alderman, witness to a grant 22 July 1471 (YASRS148/64)

Paid 8d, membership fees of Mercers' Guild, for himself and his wife, 1472 (SS129/67)

Owner of a tenement in Walmgate at the east end of Foss Bridge, occupied by Robert Yereslay. Agreement about the voidance of the waterfall of a gutter, 6 March 1474 (SS125/251)

Fined 6s 8d for wilfully disregarding a request to attend a Council meeting, 26 June 1476 (YCA B1/22)

One of a number of Aldermen who examined a case of suspected felony, 8 February 1478 (YCA B/98)

Attended a meeting of aldermen and Sheriffs of York and gentlemen of the Ainsty who agreed to help Edward IV against the Scots, 13 March 1480 (YCA B2–4/20b)

Supplied two men to accompany the Duke of Gloucester on his invasion of Scotland 14 May 1482 (YCA B2–4/58)

One of the Aldermen chosen to ride to Middleham with a present for the prince, 12 July 1483 (YCA B2–4/92)

Gave £5 in Angels as a present to the King [Richard III] and Queen on the occasion of their first visit to York, 28 August 1483 (YCA B2–4/98)

Resigned gown as Alderman 3 March 1491 and was living in 1493 (LRW/50)

Sometime master of the York Mint (H16/289)

Arms *Argent on a chevron between three leopards' heads sable three crosses crosslet fitchy argent* (SS41/17)

Father of Seth Snawshill, gentleman, Free by patrimony 1488 (SS96/213)

Father of Alice, married to John Stoker of Newington Green, and Isabel, married to John Home of Huntington (SS41/17)

Snayth, John de

Goldsmith, Free 1364 (SS96/58)

Snowden, Edward Henry

Watch and clockmaker, 21½ The Shambles (Dir 1861)

Died 25 May 1868 aged 28 buried York Cemetery grave 2703 consumption (YCReg)

South, Roger

Goldsmith, Free 1681 (SS102/156)

Soza, Martin

Goldsmith, Free 1530 (SS96/250)

Born in Saphire in Spain, naturalised 1535 (RHS)

Lived in Stonegate, wife Ellen (RHS)

Chamberlain 1535 (SS96/253)

Sheriff 1545/6 (Drake/364)

Commissioned a stained glass window for St Michael le Belfrey, 1557

(Gent/219, Drake/340)

Died 17 October 1560 buried in the south transept in York Minster, MI (Drake/494)

Owner of property in Petergate, Stonegate and Coney Street (YWCWG)

Will 10 September 1560 proved 1 February 1560, to be buried in the east choir of York Minster where Alderman White lies. Executor and legatee wife, Ellen (YASRS38/58, YWCWG)

Spari, Henry (Sperri, Sperry)

Goldsmith – one of two 'fit and prudent' goldsmiths appointed as assayers for York Mint, listed at the Trial of the Pix 2 March 1247 (Ellis/322)

Bailiff, witness to a grant 1247 (YASRS148/218)

Witness to grant, 1250x1275 (YASRS148/148 & 149)

Spendeluf, Walter (Spendofe, Spenlow)

Goldsmith, Free 1416 (SS96/124)

Witness to the will, 25 August 1429, of John Ellis (q.v.), goldsmith (YWCWG)

Searcher 1445/6 (SS120/248)

Sperry, Henry

Goldsmith

Grantor of land with buildings in Walmgate 1290x1292 (SRJ/678)

Mentioned as former proprietor of land in Walmgate 1327 (SRJ/679)

Spicer, Robert

Goldsmith

Bequeathed 20d and some tools by will of John Luneburgh (q.v.), goldsmith, 13 August 1458 (SS30/213)

Spofforth, Henry de

Goldsmith of York

Holder of a toft 'ultra Usam' [on the further side of the Ouse] paid rent (husgabel) of 2d on it, 1284 (YAJ50/88)

Sproke, Henry (Sprocke)

Goldsmith, Free 1585 (SS102/26)

Took apprentice, Joseph Maye (q.v.) 1 May 1597 (YCA D12/11b)

Squier, John

Son of Thomas Squier, apprenticed to William Seamer (q.v.) and Dorothea, his wife, indenture 15 July 1639, 7 years (YCA D12/82)

Stancliffe, John

Apprenticed to Henry Hindley (q.v.), clockmaker (Law/214)

Stead, Thomas

Son of Michael Stead, horse dealer, apprenticed to John Hampston (q.v.), John Prince (q.v.), Robert Cattle (q.v.) and George Cattle (q.v.), jewellers and silversmiths, indenture 1 October 1796, 7 years, consideration clothing and washing to be found by his father during the term of the apprenticeship (YCA D15/104)

Of Fulford Road, assay master for Goldsmiths' Company of York, working silversmith, upwards of 40 years with James Barber (q.v.) and William North (q.v.), silversmiths and jewellers, died 2 May 1839 aged 59 buried York Cemetery disease of the liver (YCReg & YG 4 May 1839)

Stephen

Goldsmith, donor of three selions of land in the parish of St Edward in the suburbs, Walmgate, which Gaudyn (q.v.), the goldsmith, leased to John de Pokelington 24 December 1303 (SRJ/3408)

Steward, Henry

Son of George Steward, without Micklegate Bar, York, comb–maker, apprenticed to Francis Agar (q.v.), clock and watchmaker, indenture 25 November 1808, 7 years (YCA D15/226)

Watchmaker, Free by order 1816 (Malden)

Watchmaker of Micklegate 1818 & 1820 (Poll)

Chosen Councillor Micklegate Ward (YkCo 25 September 1819)

Jeweller, 6 Low Ousegate (Dir 1830, 1834, 1838, 1843, 1846 & 1851)

Watchmaker, jeweller and silversmith, 6 Low Ousegate (Dir 1858)

Closing business 1 March, sale of stock, house and shop (YG 2 February 1861)

Died 28 July 1870 at 86 Bootham buried York Cemetery grave 1352 paralysis (YCReg & YG 30 July 1870)

Stock, John

see Stoke, John

Stockdale, George

Son of Robert Stockdale of York, tailor, apprentice to William Kidson (q.v.), clockmaker, indenture 27 May 1616, 12 years (YCA D12/43)

Stoke, John (Stock, Stocke)

Goldsmith, Free 1566 (SS102/7)

Married Katherine Greges 21 January 1566 St Michael le Belfrey (PReg)

Communicant with wife at St Michael le Belfrey 10 May 1573, 30 May 1574 (PReg)

Head searcher, discharged from the Common Council, 6 February 1578 (YCA B27/137b)

Award of arbitrators appointed to decide on disputes between George Kitchen and his fellow goldsmiths, Thomas Waddy (q.v.), William Pearson (q.v.), John Stock, John Raylton (q.v.) and Martin Byggyn (q.v.) 25 October 1583 (YCA B28/114)

Elected head searcher, 15 January 1583 (YCA B28/121)

Wife, Katherine, of St Michael le Belfrey, indicted for recusancy, 26 July 1584 (Aveling/204)

Buried 28 January 1598 St Michael le Belfrey (PReg)

Wife buried 28 March 1600 St Michael le Belfrey (PReg)

Stokton, William, junior

Goldsmith, son of William Stokton (q.v.), jeweller, Free by patrimony 1436 (SS96/151)

Searcher 1445/6 (SS120/248)

Father of Roger Stokton, Free by patrimony 1441 (SS96/158)

Stokton, William

Mercer, Free 1420 (SS96/129)

One of the Hospital Brethren of the Mercers' Guild 1420 (LRW/51)

Mercer, lease from mayor and commonalty of shop and rooms on Ouse

Bridge already in his tenure, rent 26s 8d per year payable from Whit Sunday 1422. To contribute to the parishioners of St Michael, Spurriergate, royal taxes and all other parish dues, 20 January 1421 (SS186/61)
Married first Alice, widow of Roger de Selby of York, spicer (SS57/33n)
Constable of Mercers' Guild 1432/3 (SS129/37)
Member, with wife, Alice, of Corpus Christi Guild 1432/3 (SS57/32)
Chamberlain 1434 (SS96/148)
Sheriff 23 June 1438 (Drake/362)
Lord Mayor 1446, 1461 (Drake/362 & RHS)
MP for York 1446 (Park/48)
Jeweller, father of William Stokton (q.v.), goldsmith, Free by patrimony 1436 (SS96/151)
Patron of a charity founded by Richard Thorne, canon of York, in St Mary's chapel, Thorne, near Beverley, 16 October 1461 (RHS)
Married second Isabella, widow of Robert Collinson, Alderman of York (SS57/33n)
Grant by him to deliver possession to John Gyliot and others of all the land which he had in the city and suburbs by feoffment from John Raghton and John Calton, 10 May 1471 (BTC16/312)
Grant by him of the advowson of Trinity hospital to John Gyliot and others, 19 May 1471 (BTC16/134)
Died intestate, administration of his estate granted 20 November 1471 buried All Saints, North Street (RHS)
Isabella's will, 20 May proved 27 July 1503, she desired to be buried in All Saints, North Street, near the bodies of her husbands (SS57/33n)

Storr, Batty

Watch and clockmaker, born 1710, youngest son of Marmaduke Batty of Selby, tanner. Married 1738 Rebecca, daughter of William White of York, hosier (Walker/87)
Clock and watchmaker of Minstergates (YkCo 23 June 1741, 29 April 1746 & 21 June 1748)
Wife, Rebecca, died in York 1753. Married second, Jane (neé Simpson), widow of John Sergeant of Hull, baker. She died in Beverley aged 71 in 1788. He died in York aged 83 in 1793 (Walker/87)
Father of Jonathan Storr (q.v.), watchmaker

Storr, Isaac

Watchmaker, born 1750, son of Batty Storr (q.v.), clock and watchmaker, died 1773 (Walker/87)

Storr, Jonathan

Watchmaker, born 1739, son of Batty Storr (q.v.), clock and watchmaker (Walker/87)
Watchmaker, Petergate (YkCo 30 August 1743 and 28 January 1755)
Married Elizabeth Skilbeck of Bedern 14 February 1768 St Michael le Belfrey (PReg)
Baptised as an adult 14 February 1768 St Michael le Belfrey (PReg)
House near First Minstergates for sale (YkCo 19 November 1771)
Elizabeth died 6 buried 8 September 1789 aged 50 St Stephen's, Acomb

cancer MI (PReg and YkCo 14 September 1789)

Died 18 buried 25 March 1805 aged 65 St Stephen's, Acomb MI (PReg and YkCo 11 March 1805)

Will dated 24 January 1804, principal beneficiary his brother William Storr (q.v.) (Loomes/172)

House etc., at the top of Stonegate for sale (YkCo 13 May 1805)

His brother, William Storr (q.v.), sold the business to Richard Dinmore (q.v.), clock and watchmaker (YkCo 15 July 1805)

Storr, William

Clockmaker of York and London, born 1743, son of Batty Storr (q.v.), clock and watchmaker (Walker/87)

Working in St Martin's in the Field, London by 1769, by which time he had a wife, Mary (Loomes/172)

Principal beneficiary under the will, dated 24 January 1804, of his brother Jonathan (q.v.) (Loomes/172)

Died and buried 8 August 1812 aged 69 at St Stephen's, Acomb MI (PReg)

Strensall, Thomas de (Strynsall)

Goldsmith

Chamberlain 1356 (SS96/49)

Bailiff 21 September 1357 (Drake/361)

Married Katherine, daughter and heir of Richard Tunnock (q.v.), goldsmith of Stonegate (RHS)

Lands in Marygate given to St Mary's Abbey by John de Cotyngham which he had had by gift from Thomas de Strensall, 4 October 1365 (CMI/226 & 227)

Paid rental of 16s for the first shop opposite the chapel on Ouse Bridge, 25 January 1376 (SS120/6)

Paid rental of 24s on land above Pavement, 25 January 1376 (SS120/2)

Paid rental of 14s on a tenement once occupied by John de Thorneton, 25 January 1376 (SS120/7)

Deceased, feoffment of a tenement in Micklegate, on the corner of North Street, from his son, William de Strynsall, to Richard de Thorneton and John Helmeslay, chaplains, 4 July 1392 (SS186/24 & 25)

Stroesburgh, Henry de

Goldsmith, Free 1391 (SS96/90)

Stultyng, John

Goldsmith

Member, with wife, Alice, of Corpus Christi Guild 1440/1 (SS57/37)

Sturgys, John de

Goldsmith, Free 1364 (SS96/59)

Suldever, Nicholas

Goldsmith, Free 1427 (SS96/139)

Surr, Richard

Son of John Surr of York, glass and chinaman, apprenticed to John Hampston (q.v.) and John Prince (q.v.), goldsmiths and jewellers, indenture 13 April 1787, 7 years, consideration £40 (YCA D15/3)

Goldsmith, Free 1794 (Malden)

Swallow, Nathaniel
Goldsmith
Free by redemption [no trade specified] 1708 (SS102/194)
Chamberlain 1713 (SS102/200)

Symonet, John
Goldsmith, Free 1387 (SS96/85)

Symson, George (Sympson)
Goldsmith, son of Radulph Symson, pewterer, Free by patrimony 1548 (SS96/269)
Father of Robert Sympson, glover, Free by patrimony 1583 (SS102/26)

Symson, James
Goldsmith, Free 1459 (SS96/178)
Father of William Symson, skinner, Free by patrimony 1481 (SS96/203)

Symson, Thomas (Simson, Sympson) *1568
Goldsmith, Free 1548 (SS96/268)
Chamberlain 1559 (SS96/279)
Of Stonegate, tenant of Martin Soza (q.v.), goldsmith, 10 September 1560 (YWCWG)
Searcher 10 April 1561 (SS186/270, YCA B23/11b)
Fined 2s 6d by the two wardens of the London company during their searches in the north, 5 February 1561 (LGC minute book K/176)
In quarantine after attending Stourbridge Fair, where the plague had been. Ordered to shut up his shop window and not consort with his neighbours. He ignored the order and was committed to ward in Monk Bar for disobedience and stubbornness until he agreed to obey the order, 15 September 1563 (YCA B23/110)
One of the collectors of first of two fifteenths and tenths from the laity of the city, 6 February 1564 (SS186/239)
Swore an oath of good workmanship and paid 3s to the London company during their searches in the north. Also paid 3s for the swearing of an oath by his servant, Thomas Howe (q.v.), 17 July 1573 (LGC minute book L/158–9)

Tailiour, Roger
Goldfiner, overseer of will of Richard Ugdon (q.v.), Master of the King's Mint in York 8 May 1545 (SS106/226 & 227)

Taillour, Thomas (Tailor, Tallor, Taylor)
Apprentice to Robert Gylmyn (q.v.), goldsmith, who paid 3s for his swearing an oath to the London company, 17 July 1573 (LGC Minute Book L/158–9)
Goldsmith, Free 1578 (SS102/19)
Of Bishophill, with wife very poor obstinate recusants, January 1595 (Aveling/218)
Of St Mary, Castlegate, with wife, Margaret, indicted for recusancy, 16 July 1596. Required to pay 3s to the poor, 6 October 1596. Indicted 10 January 1596. 3s taken 25 February 1596. Pardoned 24 June 1597 (Aveling/214–5)

Of Micklegate Ward, Bishophill junior, with wife, Margaret, recusants and non-communicants, January 1598 (Aveling/224)

Of Bishophill junior, bound for the educating of his children but refused to be bound, February 1600 (Aveling/227–8)

Of Bishophill junior, with wife, Anne, recusants, 1604 (Aveling/230)

Buried 21 June 1604 St Mary Bishophill junior (PReg)

Tesdall, William

Goldsmith, Free 1414 (SS96/121)

Tempest, Francis *1597–1616

Goldsmith, Free 1598 (SS102/41)

Administration of estate granted 13 June 1619 (YASRS38/62)

Temple, Thomas

Watchmaker and working jeweller, 3 Church Street (Dir 1867)

Terell, John

See Tirry, John

Terry, John

Clockmaker, having proposed to make a clock for the Thursday Market Cross, to the value of £25, before Martinmas (11 November) and to maintain it for seven years, to be admitted to the freedom of the city, 23 May 1706 (YCA B40/223)

To be paid 20s a year for winding the clock in Thursday Market, to commence at Candlemas (2 Feb) last, 14 April 1707 (YCA B41/12)

Father of Ruben Terry, Free by patrimony 1714 (SS102/211)

Father of Thomas Terry (q.v.), clockmaker, Free by patrimony 1734 (SS102/237)

Watchmaker, Coney Street, routed and captured a highwayman who had robbed him (YkCo 19 June 1739)

Buried 17 February 1757, St Martin, Coney Street (PReg)

Terry, John

Goldsmith.

John Busfield (q.v.), goldsmith, Coney Street, declines business in his favour (YkCo 24 May 1748)

Now following the trade of goldsmith and summoned before the Lord Mayor to show cause why he has refused to take his freedom or shut up his shop, 1 July 1748 (YCA B43/283)

Goldsmith and silversmith not being free and for following trades for which he had not having served an apprenticeship, to be prosecuted by corporation, 5 December 1748 (YCA B43/289)

Action against him deferred as he claimed he had served his father from his youth until this time in the nature of an apprenticeship but without an indenture in writing, 31 January 1748 (YCA B43/301)

No action to be taken until the recorder's opinion has been given, 1 November 1749 (YCA B43/316)

Watchmaker and silversmith, to be proceeded against for carrying on business in the city not being a freeman, 18 April 1758 (YCA B44/50)

Watchmaker, Free by order 1759 (SS102/288) on payment of £25, 27 September 1759 (YCA C40/6)

Son, John Terry, apprenticed to John Sanderson, apothecary, indenture 11 April 1763, 8 years, cancelled in the mayoralty of Richard Garland (1767–8) (YCA D14/64) but completed his time with Thomas Fowler, apothecary (Merchant Adventurer's Register of Admissions/60)

Death of wife (YkCo 1 January 1782)

Retired silversmith, died aged 87 (YkCo 3 June 1783)

House and shop in Stonegate to be let (YkCo 2 September 1783)

Terry, John

Apprenticed to Ambrose Beckwith, senior (q.v.), goldsmith, indenture 20 January 1766, 7 years, consideration £25 (PRO)

Terry, Thomas

Son of John Terry (q.v.), clockmaker, apprenticed to his father, indenture 8 May 1720, 7 years (YCA D13/53b)

Clockmaker, Free 1734 (SS102/237)

Watchmaker, married Elizabeth Priestley 31 October 1754 St Olaves (PReg)

Thackwray, James

Watchmaker and jeweller, 8 Micklegate (27 September 1856)

Moved to 106 Micklegate opposite (25 September 1858)

Jeweller of Micklegate married Althea Jane, third daughter of James Stephenson, of the Inner Temple, barrister at law (YG 21 May 1859)

Goldsmith, watchmaker etc., (YG 7 January 1860)

Theakston, Christopher

Born 2 baptised 28 August 1775 St Michael, Spurriergate (PReg)

Son of John Theakston, tinner (deceased by 1797), apprenticed to Richard Clark (q.v.), goldsmith, indenture 1 May 1790, 7 years, consideration £21 (PRO)

Jeweller, Free by patrimony [3 July] 1797 (Malden)

Jeweller of Bartholomew Square, Birmingham, 1830 (Poll)

Therasby, Peter

Watchmaker, son of William Therasby, baker, Free by patrimony 1667 (SS102/132)

Married Martha Briggs of Halifax 1668 (Loomes/177)

Thomas

The goldsmith

Witness to a grant 1185x1240 (YASRS148/58)

Grant of alms to the church of St Peter by Maud Postard, widow of Guy (q.v.), the goldsmith including a rent charge of 13s 4d owed by Thomas, which her brother, Nicholas, had given to her, 1220x1228 (YASRS148/286)

Witness to a notification of a gift by John Roman, canon of York, 1220x1228 (YASRS148/81)

Witness to a grant, 1225x1235 (YASRS148/216)

Witness to a quitclaim, 1241x1247 (YASRS148/224)

Thomas

the Goldbeater

Witness to a grant, 1270 (BTC16/91)

Thomas of the churchyard

Goldsmith, son of Josce

Grant to his younger son, Jeremy, of half his land in Petergate, lying next to the churchyard of St Peter, January 1252 (YASRS148/226)

Grant by Mariot, his widow, and Jeremy, his younger son, to Simon de Evesham, canon of York, of land with buildings in Stonegate, 1253x1261 (YASRS148/226)

Notification by William, his eldest son and heir, that a case had been brought against Simon de Evesham, archdeacon of the East Riding, over a messuage which his mother, Mariot, and his brother, Jeremy had sold him, 1253x1261 (YASRS148/227)

Notification by Simon de Evesham, archdeacon of Richmond, that he had assigned to the vicars choral his house in Stonegate which had belonged to Thomas 1262x1269/71 (YASRS148/230)

Notification of witnesses to a quitclaim made on 30 October 1266 by Jeremy, his son, to Simon de Evesham, Archdeacon of Richmond, of land and buildings in Stonegate, 1269 (YASRS148/227)

Thomas, Robert

Son of William Thomas of York, apprenticed to James Barber (q.v.) and William Whitwell (q.v.), jewellers, indenture 21 August 1819, 7 years (YCA D16/42)

Silversmith, Free 1830 (Malden)

Thomlinson, Thomas

Goldsmith, Free 1690 (SS102/167)

Thompson, Bartholomew

Silver plater of Holy Trinity, Goodramgate, parish, married Maria Wilson of the same parish 26 September 1825 Holy Trinity, Goodramgate (PReg)

Thompson, James

Son of John Thompson of York, excise officer, apprenticed to Horatio Smith (q.v.), clock and watchmaker, indenture 21 June 1824, 7 years, consideration £25 (YCA D16/134)

Thompson, John

Goldsmith

Son of Henry Thompson, wine merchant of High Ousegate and Sheriff 1602, carried on the occupation of goldsmith in a house in Coney Street, adjacent to the Mansion House (Davies/57)

Father of John Thompson (q.v.), Alderman 1683 (Davies/57)

Thompson, John (Thomson) *1635–82

Goldsmith, son of Thomas Thompson, blacksmith, Free by patrimony 1634 (SS102/85)

Search of his shop made by two wardens of London company, 8 August 1635. Parcels of plate were removed which, upon assay on 10 August, were found to be substandard. After melting down or defacing raw material returned to him upon a fine and a pledge not to offend again (LGC Minute Book Si/259–266)

Chamberlain 1659 (SS102/121)

Wife, Catherine, buried 14 May 1665 St Martin, Coney Street (PReg)

Fined for refusing office of Sheriff, 18 September 1671 (RHS)
Supplied two silver flagons to York Minster, £37 5s, 1682 (SS35/140)
Alderman 21 August 1683, displaced 5 October 1688, restored same year (RHS)
Lord Mayor 1685 (Drake/366)
Died 17 July aged 76 buried 20 July 1692 St Martin, Coney Street (PReg)
Will 20 May 1692 proved 1 April 1693 (RHS)
Watchmaker, father of Leonard Thompson (q.v.), goldsmith, Free by patrimony 1693 (SS102/172)

Thompson, John
Watchmaker
Second son of Alderman John Thompson (q.v.), goldsmith and watchmaker, baptised 12 June 1639 St Martin, Coney Street (PReg)
Married Mary ...... (RHS)
Son, Leonard, apprenticed to John Thompson (q.v.), of York goldsmith, 1 May 1685 (YCA D12/116)
Chamberlain 1699 (SS102/180)
Sheriff 1699/1700 (Drake/367)
Will 14 June 1712 proved 14 June 1714 (RHS)

Thompson, John
Jeweller, Minstergates (Dir 1843)
Surviving partner in T[homas] (q.v.) & J. Thompson, jewellers, silversmiths and watchmakers, disposed of jewellery business in all its branches to Robert Hodgson (q.v.), jeweller, but continued as watchmaker (YG 11 March 1843)

Thompson, Leonard
Goldsmith
First wife, Ellen, buried 30 May 1683 St Martin, Coney Street (PReg)
Buried St Martin, Coney Street 16 August 1698 (PReg)
Will 30 August 1698 proved 10 March 1698, bequest to his mother–in–law, Mrs Francis Fothergill,. He had property at Foggathorpe, Minstergates, and without Bootham Bar (RHS)

Thompson, Leonard
Goldsmith
[Only] son of John Thompson (q.v.), watchmaker, apprenticed to John Thompson (q.v.), goldsmith, Alderman and Lord Mayor, indenture 1 May 1685, 7 years (YCA D12/116)
Free by patrimony 1693 (SS102/172)
Married Grace, daughter of Robert and Elizabeth Gathorne of York, 30 May 1700 St Martin, Coney Street (PReg & Davies/57)
Chamberlain 1703 (SS102/185)
Sheriff 1706/7 (Drake/367)
Buried St Martin, Coney Street, 1 December 1711 (PReg)
Will 2 September 1705 proved 22 January 1711(RHS)
Will of wife, Elizabeth, 27 November 1719, bequeathed the house in Coney Street to Francis Taylor, gentleman (Davies/57)

Thompson, Roger
Goldsmith, son of William Thompson, smith, Free by patrimony 1552 (SS96/273)

Thompson, Thomas
Eldest son of Thomas Thompson of Grove Lodge (YG 21 January 1843)
Jeweller of St Olaves parish married Mary Ann Colley of St Maurice parish 6 September 1835 at St Maurice (PReg)
Working jeweller of Townend Street (Dir 1838)
Watchmaker and jeweller of Petergate, in partnership with brother, John Thompson (q.v.) (YG 11 March 1843)
Died 15 January 1843 aged 31 York Cemetery grave 3904 decline (YCReg)

Thornton, John
Son of Thomas Thornton of Great Hutton, yeoman, apprenticed to William Thornton (q.v.), clockmaker, indenture 27 December 1752, 7 years (YCA D13/115b)

Thornton, William
Son of Thomas Thornton of Great Hutton, apprenticed to Henry Hindley (q.v.), clockmaker, indenture 1 May 1741, 7 years (YCA D13/99 & 99b)
Clockmaker without Micklegate Bar, 2 February 1756 (YCA D13/125b)
House without Micklegate Bar for sale (YkCo 17 March 1761)
Imprisoned in the Kidcote, required to deliver to the court a schedule of his estates and effects for the benefit of his creditors, suit executed by Thomas Thornton (YkCo 15 September 1761)
Took his final apprentice, Alex Mason (q.v.), 16 August 1762 (PRO)

Thorparche, Richard de
Goldsmith of York
Grant to him by David, son of William the reeve of Thorparch, of one acre of arable land in Alwardesgarthes in Walmgate near the hospital of St Nicholas, 30 July 1348 (BTC16/128)
Grant by John Clement of York, currier, and Agnes his wife, executors of his testament, to Walter de Holdernesse of York and Matilda his wife, of three selions of land in Walmgate in the suburbs which he had bequeathed to be sold, 9 September 1351 (BTC16/128 & 129)

Thwayt, Thomas de
Goldbeater
Of St Michael le Belfrey parish, paid poll tax of 2s 0d with wife, Isabella, 1381 (Bartlett/48)
Probate granted on his estate 16 July 1395 (YASRS6/169)

Thwaytes, Richard
Goldsmith, Free 1446 (SS96/165)

Tiler, Chamberlain
Silversmith, father of William Tiler (q.v.), an apprentice to John Hampston (q.v.) and John Prince (q.v.), goldsmiths and jewellers, 1778 (YCA D14/191)

Tiler, William
Son of Chamberlain Tiler of York, silversmith, apprenticed to John

Hampston (q.v.) and John Prince (q.v.), goldsmiths and jewellers, indenture 2 February 1778, 7 years (YCA D14/191)

Tirry, John (Tirell, Tirre, Terell, Tyrre)

Goldsmith, Free 1468 (SS96/288)

Witness to the will, 2 August 1467, of William Rotherham (q.v.), goldsmith (YWCWG)

Concerned in a slander. He had heard Thomas Welles (q.v.) say that Herman Goldsmith (q.v.) was a 'false theiff', 14 November 1476 (YCA B1/13b)

Bound himself, amongst others, for £20 to carry out the judgement of arbiters, June 1478 (Attreed/167)

Todd, James

Goldsmith, son of Samuel Todd, milliner, Free by patrimony 1671 (SS102/139)

Father of Samuel Todd, Free by patrimony 1708 (SS012/194)

Father of James Todd, barber, Free by patrimony 1741 (SS102/260)

Todd, John

Clockmaker, Free 1665 (SS102/131)

Todd, Samuel

Watchmaker, son of Samuel Todd, milliner, Free by patrimony 1686 (SS102/163)

Todd, William (Tod)

Goldsmith, Free 1560 (SS102/1)

Swore an oath of good workmanship and paid 3s to the London company during their searches in the north. Also paid 3s for the swearing of oaths by his servants John Sharre (q.v.) and John Mady (q.v.), 17 July 1573 (LGC minute book L/158–9)

With wife enjoined to continue their conformity and dismissed by the recusancy commission, 5 October 1580 (Aveling/191)

Tolson, Wilfrid

Baptised 10 September 1664

Jeweller, took apprentice Benjamin Langwith (q.v.) 26 Feb 1720 (YCA D13/13b)

Of Lendal (next to the Mansion House) 1727 (Cossins's map)

Wife, Margaret, buried 17 April 1726 St Martin, Coney Street (PReg)

Married, second, Mrs Mary Rhodes 28 August 1726 Holy Trinity, King's Court (PReg) widow of Charles Rho[a]des (q.v.), goldsmith.

Buried 4 February 1732 St Martin, Coney Street (PReg)

Will proved 17 April 1733

Tomlinson, John

Stepson of William Littlewood of Selby, ship's carpenter, apprenticed to Horatio Smith (q.v.), clock and watchmaker, indenture 14 August 1833, 7 years (D16/332)

Watchmaker, 65 Walmgate (Dir 1851)

Topham, William

Son of Benjamin Topham of Thirsk, tailor, apprenticed to John Hampston (q.v.) and John Prince (q.v.), goldsmiths and jewellers, indenture 2 October

1778, 8 years (YCA D14/206)

Jeweller, Free 1787 (Malden)

Wife, Mary Ann, only child and heir of John Day, late of Acomb, gentleman, seised as tenant in tail of a messuage in Clifton, tenanted by Samuel Lockwood and William Nelson, gardener, as well as 5 acres in Clifton moor, 23 December 1791 (YASRS137/360)

Councillor Micklegate Ward, died aged 32 (YH 30 September 1797)

Traves, James (Travas)

Goldsmith, Free 1470 (SS96/190)

Member, with wife, Johanna, of Corpus Christi Guild 1471 (SS57/80)

Triton, Radalph de

Goldbeater, Free 1333 (SS96/27)

Tritschler, Bernard

Watchmaker and dealer in jewellery, 12 Stonegate, aged 33, born in Scollach, Baden, proprietor of M Kleiser & Co., employing 2 men, including Matthew Wehrly (q.v.), and 1 apprentice, Severin Heine (1871 Census)

Wife Anna Cecilia (born London) died 2 April 1872 aged 24 buried York Cemetery grave 11366 consumption (YCReg)

Firm eventually became M. Wehrly & Co, watch and clockmakers, jewellers etc. (YG 14 July 1883)

Tunnock, Richard (Tunnoc)

Goldsmith (RHS) and bellfounder

Bailiff 1320/1 (Drake/360)

Granted St Peter Prison at Minstergates, with an annual rental to be paid to the prebendary of Osbaldwick, the Dean and Chapter, and St Leonard's hospital, 1311/12 (CRP 1307–13/431)

MP for York 1327 (Park/42)

Founded a chantry (one of six) at the altar of St Thomas the Martyr in York Minster (NW side of NW pillar of the central tower) endowed with 4 marks a year out of the house in which he lived in Stonegate, 1328 (SS35/303 & CRP 5 1327–30/309)

Owner of property in Stonegate (copyhold), North Street, Ousegate and Skeldergate (YML Wills 1/8b)

Will 10 July proved 17 July 1330, to be buried in York Minster before the altar of St Thomas the Martyr. Left a silver cup with cover, a great maser with silver foot and a silver piece. Executor and residuary legatee wife, Agnes (YASRS38/64 & YML Wills 1/8b)

Katharine, his daughter and eventual heiress married Thomas de Strensall (q.v.), goldsmith (RHS)

Turner, Daniel *1702

Goldsmith, son of Henry Turner, whitesmith, Free by patrimony 1701 (SS102/183)

Father of Henry Turner, barber surgeon and periwig maker, Free by patrimony 1725 (SS102/224)

Turner, Thomas

Goldsmith, son of Edward Turner, gentleman, Free by patrimony 1581

(SS102/22)

With others lay in wait and assaulted the Archbishop's men as they returned from York to Bishopthorpe, committed to ward during the pleasure of the Lord Mayor and bound over to keep the peace, 30 December 1581 (YCA B28/35b)

Presented a bill for 29s 4d for new flourishing and trimming the escutcheons and chains belonging to the City Waits. The chamberlains to pay so much of the bill as they think good, 17 February 1584 (YCA B28/3)

1584/5 for making the escutcheons for the waits' collars 5s, for making and amending 4 chains 6s 8d, for mending 4 badges and gilding the rest 8s, for one ounce and a half of silver for the same 7s 4d – total 27s (Jewitt/464)

1585/6 For mending the cross on the city's little mace 12d (Jewitt/458)

Tyso, John

Goldsmith, Free 1479 (SS96/201)

Debt of 40d pending on chamberlains' accounts payable to John Sponer, sergeant at mace, 6 October 1479, still pending 2 December 1479 (Attreed/182 & 186)

Ugdon, Richard

Master of King's Mint in York

Will 8 May proved 18 June 1545, desired to be buried at Holy Trinity Goodramgate. Witnesses, George Gale (q.v.), goldsmith, Richard Lee (q.v.), assayer, William Myrfyne (q.v.), his cousin, finer. Overseer Roger Tailiour (q.v.), goldfiner (SS106/226 & 227)

Ulveston, John de

Goldsmith, Free 1355 (SS96/50)

Upsale, John de (Upsall)

Goldsmith, Free 1374 (SS96/71)

Paid rental of 8s for the second shop opposite the chapel on Ouse Bridge, 25 January 1376 (SS120/6)

Of St John's, Ouse Bridge, parish, paid poll tax of 12d, 1381 (Bartlett/61)

Vanconehonen, Henry

Goldsmith, Free 1446 (SS96/165)

Veal, Bernard U. *

A Polish refugee, opened a workshop in New Street 1932, having learnt his craft from Mr M.P. Jacobs of Brighton, a former London silversmith. Eventually moved to 6 Coney Street, then Shambles and then, in 1944, to 44 Stonegate. Business closed 1 September 1984 (YEP 21 April & 20 August 1984)

Registered his mark, BUV, with Sheffield Assay Office 21 March 1933 (letter from librarian at Sheffield Assay Office)

Vincent, William

Watchmaker, Free by order 1764 (SS102/72)

Partnership with William Clarke (q.v.), clock and watch maker, dissolved (YkCo 17 July 1764)

Married Bettina Steventon, wealthy daughter of late Anthony Steventon,

of London, goldsmith and banker, 31 December 1772 St Michael le Belfrey (PReg, YCh 1 January 1773 & YkCo 5 January 1773)
Watchmaker, shop in High Ousegate 1774–84, Pavement 1790–97 (Loomes/183, Poll & Dir 1798)
Death of wife (YH 16 March 1793)
Death aged 63 (YH 30 September 1797)

Waddy, Thomas (Waddie) *1576
Goldsmith, Free 1572 (SS102/13)
Of Monk ward, representative of the goldsmiths' craft on the Common Council of the city, May 1579 (YCA B27/160b)
George Kitchin (q.v.), goldsmith informed the council that William Pearson (q.v.) and Thomas Waddy (who had just replaced Martin Byggyn (q.v.)), searchers, had refused to mark his plate with the touch, 10 May 1583 (YCA B28/97)
Award of arbitrators appointed to decide on disputes between George Kitchen and his fellow goldsmiths, Thomas Waddy, William Pearson (q.v.), John Stock (q.v.), John Raylton (q.v.) and Martin Byggyn (q.v.) 25 October 1583 (YCA B28/114)
Replaced as searcher 5 January 1583 (YCA B28/121)
Sold ale contrary to the rates and assize set by the Lord Mayor, discharged from selling ale 27 November 1587 (B29/236)

Wadkin, Joseph
Son of John Wadkin, porter, apprenticed to James Barber (q.v.) and William North (q.v.), silversmiths and jewellers, indenture 5 November 1839, 7 years (YCA D16/397)

Waggitt, Charles (Waggett)
Son of Michael Waggitt (q.v.), clockmaker, apprenticed to Thomas Agar (q.v.), clock and watchmaker, indenture 8 June 1804, 7 years 4 months and 18 days, no consideration (YCA D15/179), later assigned to John Agar (q.v.), son of Thomas Agar (Malden)
Watchmaker, Free 1812 (Malden)
Watchmaker of Petergate 1818 (Poll)
Married Mary Birch 22 January 1820 Holy Trinity, Goodramgate (PReg and YG 29 January 1820)
Watchmaker of Skeldergate (Poll 1820)
Clock and watchmaker, 65 Skeldergate (Dir 1828), 2 Micklegate (Dir 1830)
Moved from 2 Micklegate to 14 Bridge Street (YG 14 July 1838)
Died 8 September 1857 aged 66 buried York Cemetery grave 13187 diarrhoea (YCReg and YG 12 September 1857)
Wife, Mary, died 2 January 1862 aged 71 buried York Cemetery grave 13187 natural decay (YCReg)

Waggitt, George William
Watchmaker, son of Charles Waggitt (q.v.), watchmaker
Watchmaker of Bridge Street, died 13 December 1872 aged 52 buried York Cemetery grave 13187 natural decay (YCReg and YG 21 December 1872)

Widow, Hannah, of Nunnery Lane died 13 May 1883 aged 58 buried York Cemetery grave 13187 disease of liver (YCReg)

Waggitt, Michael
Clockmaker of Fossgate, son of Michael Waggitt of Richmond, clockmaker. Married Ann daughter of ..... Wastell of Stainmoor, carrier. Eighth child and fifth son baptised St Crux, 1806 (PReg)

Waite, John
Goldsmith, son of John Waite, glover, Free by patrimony 1617 (SS102/67)

Waite, Richard
Goldsmith, son of Thomas Waite (q.v.), goldsmith (Free 1614), Free by patrimony 1640 (SS102/93)
His wife, Anne, and children were living in 1663 (RHS)

Waite, Thomas *1630–53
Goldsmith, Free 1614 (SS102/62)
One of the witnesses to the will of Christopher Harrington (q.v.), goldsmith, 11 November 1614 (Rel/213)
Search of his shop made by two wardens of London company, 8 August 1635. Parcels of plate were removed which, upon assay on 10 August, were found to be substandard. After melting down or defacing raw material returned to him upon a fine and a pledge not to offend again (LGC Minute Book Si/259–266)
Chamberlain 1640 (SS102/93)
Father of Richard Waite (q.v.), goldsmith, Free by patrimony 1640 (SS102/93)
Sheriff 10 November 1652 (Drake/366 & RHS)
Will 18 February 1662, to be buried in St Michael, Spurriergate (YASRS49/97)
Father of William Waite (q.v.), goldsmith, Free by patrimony 1653 (SS102/115)

Waite, Thomas
Goldsmith, died 1695 (Jackson/299)

Waite, William *1657
Goldsmith, son of Thomas Waite (q.v.), gentleman [goldsmith], Free by patrimony 1653 (SS102/115)
Chamberlain 1664 (SS102/128)
Married Mrs Stamper 17 January 1666/7 Methley (RHS)

Walding, Peter
Goldsmith
Of St Edward in the suburbs parish, Walmgate, grant to Robert, perpetual vicar of St Laurence, of a house in Walmgate 1250x1299 (BTC16/105)
Grant by his son, Gaudin, to Eudo de Toutorp of all his land in Walmgate in St Edward in the suburbs parish, 1275x1299 (BTC16/109)
Grant to his son, Walding, by Nicholas Orger of all his land in Walmgate in St Edward in the suburb parish, 7 May 1282 (BTC16/109)
Grant to his daughter Mariota by John, son of Gaudin the goldsmith (q.v.), of a messuage in Walmgate, 13 June 1304 (BTC16/106)

Walker, Robert

Born and baptised 13 January 1800 St Helen, Stonegate (PReg)

Watchmaker of Beverley, son of John Walker [of Davygate 1800], yeoman, Free by patrimony [30 January] 1821 (Malden)

Watchmaker of Beverley 1830 (Poll)

Walker, Robert

Born Glasgow 1828 (Loomes/185)

Watchmaker and jeweller, five years with James Barber (q.v.), watch and clockmaker, silversmith and jeweller (YG 17 December 1859)

With Robert Heselgrave (q.v.), another former employee, purchased Barber & Co, 25/26 Coney Street (renumbered 13 by 1872) from James Silburn Barber (q.v.) at auction (YG 6 July 1859 & Gubbins/19)

Walker and Heselgrave, jewellers, silversmiths and watchmakers (YG 10 September 1859)

Watchmaker and jeweller, opened his own shop at 56 Coney Street, opposite the Mansion House (YG 17 December 1859)

Of 22 Spurriergate (YG 26 October 1867)

House and shop at 16 (old 22) Spurriergate for sale (YG 24 May 1875)

Of 55 Stonegate (Dir 1879)

Wife, Jane, died 16 December 1902 aged 76 buried York Cemetery grave 3070 natural decay (YCReg)

Watchmaker and jeweller of 55 Stonegate, died 7 May 1913 aged 85 buried York Cemetery grave 3070 senile decay (YG 10 May 1913)

Wallys, Christopher

Goldsmith, Free 1518 (SS96/240)

Walselenen, Wyttecon (Witkynus)

Goldsmith, Free 1378 (SS96/75)

Of St Michael le Belfrey parish, paid poll tax [amount illegible] 1381 (Bartlett/61)

Walter

Son of Lodwin, leased land in The Marsh [Hungate], 1180x1190 (EYC 1/229 & 230)

Owed £62 on all his lands to Aaron the Jew, 1191 (Pipe Rolls Soc NS2/23)

Maud Aubyn, his daughter, was in possession of property in St Andrewgate in the time of Richard [1189–1199], certified 4 May 1361 (CCR/172)

Walter

The goldsmith, otherwise the goldbeater, witness to grants 1220x1228 (YASRS148/3), c.1230 (YASRS148/4)

Walter

The goldsmith, owner of property in Goodramgate, next to the Holy Trinity churchyard and in Ispingayl [Spen Lane] in the tenancy of Eudo the butcher who paid a rental of 6d, 1260 (Drake/620)

Witness to a grant 1247x1262 (YASRS148/225)

Witness to a quitclaim 1269 (YASRS148/227)

Witness to grants 20 July 1278 (YASRS148/209), 16 October 1278

(YASRS148/231), 1279x1285/6 (YASRS148/232), 8 May 1290 (YASRS148/237), 1 May 1292 (YASRS148/11)

Ward, Henry

Born 27 baptised 28 July 1807 Holy Trinity, King's Court (PReg)

Watchmaker, son of John Ward, aledraper, Free by patrimony [17 July] 1830 (Malden)

Watchmaker of King's Square 1830 (Poll)

Married Harriet, youngest daughter of the late Mr Bromley, coal merchant (YG 7 April 1838)

Watchmaker, 8 King's Square (Dir 1838), 24 Parliament Street (Dir 1841)

Watchmaker and jeweller, 2 Nessgate (Dir 1843)

Watchmaker, King's Staithe (Dir 1849) 6 Coney Street (Dir 1855), 11 College Street (Dir 1867)

Died 5 November 1876 aged 69 (YG 11 November 1876)

Ward, Henry Baines

Watchmaker and silversmith, died (YG 18 April 1903)

Watchmaker and jeweller died 9 April 1903 aged 48 buried York Cemetery grave 16064 suicide by poison (YCReg)

Ward, Robert

Working jeweller, 6 Coney Street (Dir 1851) 5 Davygate (Dir 1858, 1861 & 1867)

Warter, Richard (Watre, Wartere, Wartyr)

Goldsmith, Free 1415 (SS96/124)

Son of William and Johanna Warter who were buried at Bugthorpe (YWCWG)

Married first Alice Lokton (RHS) her will 20 August proved 6 September 1421, buried St Michael le Belfrey (YASRS38/67, YWCWG)

Married second Alice daughter of John Moreton, Alderman of York (She had died before 21 May 1458) (YWCWG)

Member, with wife, Alice, of Corpus Christi Guild 1423/4 (SS57/23)

Chamberlain 1426 (SS96/137)

Sheriff 1431 (Drake/362)

MP for York 1435 (Park/48)

Lord Mayor 1436 & 1451 (Drake/362 & 363)

Will 21 May 1458 proved 8 March 1464, buried in the south aisle of St Saviour near Alice, his second wife, under a stone which he had put there, inscribed with his armorial. Left two silver dishes, standing cup with lid, silver and gilt goblet, small bowl, and two other silver pieces to be kept in a chest to be kept in York Minster vestry. Keys to be held by executors who were all to be present when opened (YASRS6/178, YWCWG)

Waryn, William

Jeweller, Free 1420 (SS96/129)

Watson, Christopher

Jeweller, son of Robert Watson, teadealer (deceased), Free by patrimony 1810 (Malden)

Upwards of 11 years with Cattle and Barber, opens a business as a working jeweller in premises adjacent to the White Swan (YkCo 22

August 1814)

Assays of York 1814–21 (YAJ49/121)

Silversmith and jeweller, Pavement (Dir 1818)

Married Miss Bell of the Angel Inn, Easingwold at All Saints, Pavement (YCh 15 October 1818)

Working jeweller, goldsmith, watchmaker, dealer in old coins, medals and china, moved from Pavement to spacious new premises in New Bridge Street, corner of Skeldergate (YCh 10 December 1818)

Took apprentice, his brother–in–law John Bell (q.v.), indenture 25 January 1819 (YCA D16/33)

Working goldsmith, jeweller and watch–maker, dealer in cut glass, genuine teas etc., moved from corner of Skeldergate to the house immediately adjacent to Wentworth, Challoner & Co's bank in Low Ousegate (YG 13 April 1822)

Goldsmith, silversmith and working jeweller, 14 Low Ousegate (Dir 1823 & 1830)

Goldsmith, jeweller and silversmith to HRH the Duke of Sussex (YG 24 March 1827)

John Bell, ex–apprentice, taken into partnership (YG 8 May 1832)

Watson and Bell, 17 Low Ousegate (Dir 1838 & 1843)

Jewellers and silversmiths to HRH the Duke of Sussex (YG 2 June 1838)

Retired 1 April 1844 (YG 2 December 1843)

His wife, last surviving sister of Mr Bell, died aged 57 (YG 1 March 1845)

One of the trustees of a company which published 'The Yorkshireman' newspaper, 1848 (Malden – see Brown, George)

Watson, Edward

Goldsmith, son of Edward Watson, mercer, Free by patrimony 1638 (SS102/90)

Watson, Henry

Born 22 June baptised 8 July 1787 All Saints, Pavement (PReg)

Silversmith, [fourth] son of William Watson of Heslington [of Jubbergate 1787], bricklayer (deceased), Free by patrimony [21 February] 1809 (Malden)

Silversmith of Jubbergate 1820, of Cherry Grove 1830 (Poll)

57 years with Barber, Cattle and North (YG 19 January 1867)

Silversmith of Cemetery Road died 3 January 1867 aged 82 buried York Cemetery grave 3269 old age (YCReg)

Watson, John

Goldsmith, Free 1416 (SS96/123)

Watson, John

Goldsmith, Free 1419 (SS96/127)

Born in Scotland became a naturalised Englishman on the surety of William Herte of York, spurrier, 2 September 1419 (SS125/115)

Watson, Richard

Apprenticed to John Hampston (q.v.), John Prince (q.v.), Robert Cattle (q.v.) and George Cattle (q.v.), jewellers, indenture 17 May 1796, 7 years, consideration £16 (PRO)

Watson, Thomas

Goldsmith, son of Henry Watson, fishmonger (Free 1437), Free by patrimony 1461 (SS96/181)

Watson, William

Son of George Watson, apprenticed to Robert Clark (q.v.), watchmaker, indenture 21 March 1808, 7 years, consideration £10 plus 1 year's board and lodging (YCA D15/218)

Watchmaker, Free 1815 (Malden)

Watchmaker of Stonegate 1820, of Low Ousegate 1830 (Poll)

Publican of the Joiner's Arms, 18 Goodramgate (Dir 1851)

Formerly kept a public house in York, had opened a watchmaking business in Kirk Hammerton by November 1853 (YG 5 November 1853)

Watson, William Peter

Son of Elizabeth Watson, widow, apprenticed to Ambrose Beckwith, senior (q.v.), jeweller and goldsmith, indenture 2 May 1770, 8 years, consideration faithful service (PRO)

Wawton, Richard (Walton, Waulton)

Goldsmith, Free 1554 (SS96/275)

Buried January 1566 St Michael le Belfrey (PReg)

Will 15 January 1566 proved 21 April 1567, to be buried 'as near Master Crawfurthe as maybe' at St Michael le Belfrey. Supervisor of will and guardian of his two children, Christopher Hunton (q.v.), goldsmith (YASRS38/67, YWCWG)

Father of Matthew Walton, tiler, Free by patrimony 1590 (SS102/33)

Waynd, Richard

Watchmaker, Free 1667 (SS102/133)

Webb, William

For gilding the weather vanes at York Minster and providing iron staples for them, a part of 8s 8d, 1485 (see John Colayne) (SS35/88)

Wehrly, Matthew

Watch repairer unmarried aged 25 born Hammereisbach, Baden, lodging with Bernard Tritschler (q.v.), watchmaker and dealer in jewellery, 12 Stonegate, who was the proprietor of M. Kleiser & Co (1871 Census) which eventually became M. Wehrly & Co, watch and clockmakers, jewellers etc. (YG 14 July 1883)

Watchmaker and senior partner (junior partner, Severin Heine) employing 1 man and 2 apprentices, including Roman Wehrly (1881 Census)

Last appearance in Electoral Register, 4 October 1888

Wellyng, John

Goldsmith, Free 1412 (SS96/116)

Welles, Robert

Goldsmith, son of Thomas Welles (q.v.), goldsmith (Free 1460), Free by patrimony 1500 (SS96/224)

Left, by the will of his father, proved 15 June 1500, all the tools pertaining to their work (YWCWG)

Welles, Thomas (Wells, Wellys)

Goldsmith, Free 1460 (SS96/180)

A person of this name was admitted a member of Mercers' Guild, 1468 (Cartulary/3) and paid 4d, membership fee of Mercers' Guild 1472 (SS129/67) [This may be Thomas Welles, merchant, Free 1464 (SS96/184)]

Concerned in a slander. He said that Herman Goldsmith (q.v.) was a 'false theiff', 14 November 1476 (YCA B1/13b)

Paid for adding new gold to the mayor's mace 6s 8d, 1478/9 (SS192/165)

With others bound himself with a surety of £10 each to ensure that Robert Levysam, mercer, would do no harm to Thomas Beyn, capmaker, 9 October 1483 (Attreed/719)

With others bound himself with a surety of £10 each to ensure that John Peghan, mercer, would do no damage or bodily harm to Richard Doweson, clerk, 2 January 1484 (Attreed/423)

Member of an inquest jury to enquire into the lands of the late John Gilliot, merchant, 7 November 1486 (Attreed/499 & 500)

Witness to a sale document, 1486/7 (YASRS148/262)

Paid 10s for the fourth place, in front of his house at the junction of Skeldergate and Micklegate, on the Corpus Christi pageant route, 1486/7 (SS192/180)

With Richard Croklyn bound himself with a surety of £10 each to ensure that Robert Flaxton would do no damage etc., to Roland Brise, June 1487 (Attreed/581)

Appointed one of the arbiters to hear the case of William Mason, vintner and Henry Topham, fuller, 3 January 1489 (Attreed/613)

Chamberlain 1489 (SS96/213)

With others received, in the council chamber on Ouse Bridge, a silk girdle from Sir Thomas Bridlington, vicar of Barton in Westmorland, on behalf of the Corpus Christi Guild, 7 September 1491 (SS57/281)

Examined as a witness to an assault on Sheriff, Richard Thornton, by Ralph Neville outside his house at the junction of Skeldergate and Micklegate 27 July 1496 (YCA B8/6b & 7)

Father of Agnes Welles, a nun, prioress of Clementhorpe (YWCWG)

Undated will proved 15 June 1500, to be buried by St James' altar in his parish church. Executor and legatee wife, Elizabeth. All the tools pertaining to his work left to his son Robert Welles (q.v.) (YASRS6/181, YWCWG)

Whip, John

Son of William Whip, coal merchant, apprenticed to John Hampston (q.v.), John Prince (q.v.), Robert Cattle (q.v.) and George Cattle (q.v.), jewellers and silversmiths, indenture 4 October 1799, 7 years (YCA D15/132)

Silversmith, Free 1820 (Malden)

Silversmith of Coney Street 1820 (Poll)

Whit, William

Goldsmith

Will 16 April 1506 proved [no date], to be buried at St John Evangelist

[Ouse Bridge], next to father's tomb (YASRS6/183, YWCWG)

Whitehill, Christopher (Whithill) *1685–89
Goldsmith, son of John Whitehill, bricklayer, Free by patrimony 1677 (SS102/149)
Father of Christopher Whitehill, Free by patrimony 1714 (SS102/206)

Whitwell, William *
Son of James Whitwell of Scoresby, apprenticed to James Bellamy Carlill (q.v.), watchmaker, indenture 17 June 1802, 7 years, consideration £70 (YCA D15/160)
Taken into partnership by James Barber (q.v.), jeweller, 1 January 1814 (YkCo 24 October 1814)
Married Mary Elizabeth, eldest daughter of William Staveley, governor of York Castle (YkCo 11 November 1816)

Children baptised at St Martin, Coney Street, 1818–23 (PReg)
Died 24 April 1823 aged 36 after a painful illness (YG 26 April 1823)
Widow married George Cattle (q.v.), silversmith (YG 6 November 1824)

Whixlay, Thomas
Goldsmith, Free 1440 (SS96/155)

Whyt Richard
Goldsmith, Free 1389 (SS96/87)

Widder, Thomas
Goldsmith, Free 1441 (SS96/158)

Wigglesworth, Henry
Goldsmith, Free 1630 (SS102/80)

Wilberfosse, Peter de
Goldbeater, Free 1375 (SS96/73)

Wiles, Henry
Jeweller, 10 High Ousegate (Dir 1846)

Wilkinson, Thomas
Clockmaker of York, 1750, died 1776 (Dinsdale/82)

Willerdby, George
Goldsmith, Free 1445 (SS96/163)

Willerton, William
Goldsmith, appraiser of the inventory of Thomas Morton, canon residentiary of York, 13 June 1449 (YML Add MS L1/17/44)

William

the Goldbeater

Owner of land in St Gregory's parish, Micklegate, 1200x1225 (YASRS148/160)

Witness to a document 1180x1250 (SRJ/1729)

William

The goldsmith, witness to a grant, 1250x1275 (YASR148/147)

Witness to documents, 1273x1274 (SRJ/13), 1291 (SRJ/2612)

William

Goldsmith of York

Paid poll tax of 6d on property in St Dennis parish valued at 10s, 1327 (YASRS74/162)

Of St Dennis parish, paid 8d poll tax 1334 (YkHist 13/8)

William

Goldsmith of York

Possibly the kinsman of Alan de Alnwyck (q.v.) who under the terms of his will, 3 September 1374, was to inherit the tools of the craft when he attained the age of 20 (YWCWG/37)

Witness to documents, 1394 (SRJ/2881, 2882 & 2883)

Of Fossgate, mentioned in connection with a debt of 2s 4d in the inventory of Geoffrey and Idonea Couper of Goodramgate, 1402 (YML Add MS L1/17/24)

Williamson, John

Goldsmith

Searcher, debt of 4s 4d pending on chamberlains' accounts payable to John Fery, sergeant at mace, 6 October 1476. Debt settled (Attreed/20)

Williamson, John

Goldsmith, son of John Williamson, mariner, Free by patrimony 1674 (SS102/146)

Paid Hearth Tax on 5 hearths in a house in St Michael le Belfrey parish, 1671 (Hearth/12)

Father of William Williamson, Free by patrimony 1695 (SS102/175)

Chamberlain 1696 (SS102/175)

Died 14 January 1703, MI St Michael, Spurriergate (Wilson/247)

Father of Jane Williamson, Free by patrimony 1706 (SS102/190)

Williamson, Robert

Goldsmith, son of Geoffrey Williamson, draper, Free by patrimony 1597 (SS102/41)

Williamson, Robert *1623–38

Goldsmith, son of Peter Williamson, saddler, Free by patrimony 1624 (SS/102/74)

Search of his shop made by two wardens of London company, 8 August 1635. Parcels of plate were removed which, upon assay on 10 August, were found to be substandard. After melting down or defacing raw material returned to him upon a fine and a pledge not to offend again (LGC Minute Book Si/259–266)

Chamberlain 1646 (SS102/102)

Subject of a complaint from the Spurriers that he and others were selling spurs. Forbidden under penalty from doing so, 14 September 1646 (YCA B36/194)

Father of Robert Williamson (q.v.), goldsmith, Free by patrimony 1653 (SS102/115)

Williamson, Robert *1655–90

Goldsmith, son of Robert Williamson (q.v.), goldsmith (Free 1624), Free by patrimony 1653 (SS102/115)

Paid Hearth Tax on 4 hearths in a house in St Martin, Coney Street, parish, 1671 (Hearth/20)

Six money boxes bought from him by Edward Malt on behalf of Major John Wallis who claimed expenses, on 17 May 1671, of £8 1s 1d from the wardens of the London company. These expenses included other items bought from Thomas Mangy (q.v.) and Rowland Kirby (q.v.) as well as carriage and letters (LGC Court Book 6/196–7)

Father of Robert Williamson, Free by patrimony 1707 (SS102/192)

Williamson, William

Goldsmith, Free, 1551 (SS96/272)

Williamson, William *1704–9

Son [trade not stated] of John Williamson (q.v.), goldsmith (Free 1675), Free by patrimony 1695 (SS102/175)

A Mr Williamson appeared before court of London company for selling substandard silver wares. Ordered to pay 20s, the cost of the goods, and £3 4s charges, 6 October 1699 (LGC Court Book 10/205)

Wilson, James

Son of Robert Wilson of York, apprenticed to Charles Waggitt (q.v.), clock and watchmaker, indenture 26 September 1849, 7 years, consideration £29 (YCA D16/481)

Watchmaker of Goodramgate, died 11 September 1849 aged 30 buried York Cemetery grave 6199 disease of the heart (YCReg)

Wilson, Richard

Clockmaker, Free as a locksmith 1586 (SS102/27)

Father of William Wilson (q.v.), clockmaker, Free by patrimony 1608 (SS102/56)

Wilson, Thomas (Willson)

Goldsmith, Free 1504 (SS96/228)

Will 2 March proved 28 June 1516, to be buried St Michael, Spurriergate. Executor and legatee wife, Margaret (YASRS11/200, YWCWG)

Wilson, William (Wylson)

Goldsmith, son of John Wilson, cordwainer, Free by patrimony 1491 (SS96/216)

Married first Alice, daughter of Robert Denton of York (SS57/135n)

Member, with wife, Alice, of Corpus Christi Guild 1492 (SS57/135)

Married second Elizabeth, daughter of William White, Alderman of York (SS157/135n)

Chamberlain 1504 (SS96/228)

Sheriff 1505/6 (Drake/363)

Alderman 10 November 1508 (RHS)
Lord Mayor 1513 (SS96/235)
With his alderman in scarlet gowns and the 24 in crimson gowns, met the Earl of Surrey at Marygate end outside Bootham Bar, 20 September 1513. The earl was accompanying the dead body of King of Scotland [James IV] to London (YCA B9/71b)
Died 1516/17 (SS57/135n), will 10 September proved 25 September 1517, to be buried in St Michael, Spurriergate, on south side of sepulchre of Alderman Robert Johnson, merchant. Bequest to his wife, Elizabeth, of the messuage he then dwelt in upon Ouse bridge with all the lands and tenements belonging to it recently purchased from Sir William Fairfax of Steeton. Left nut with silver and gilt cover. Executor and legatee wife Elizabeth (YASRS11/206, YWCWG)
Father of William Wilson, corn chapman, Free by patrimony 1545 (SS96/265)

Wilson, William
Son of Richard Wilson, clockmaker, Free by patrimony 1608 (SS102/1585)

Wilton, John
Goldsmith of York
Of Holy Trinity, Goodramgate, parish, paid poll tax [amount illegible] with Alicia, his wife 1381 (Bartlett/61)

Wood, George
Son of Francis Wood, widow, apprenticed to Christopher Watson (q.v.), jeweller, indenture 13 January 1823, 7 years (YCA D16/106)
Jeweller, Free 1830 (Malden)
Jeweller of Micklegate 1830 (Poll)
Jeweller, 1 New York Street (Dir 1851)
Last Assay Master, York Goldsmiths' Company c.1857 (Gubbins/47)
Assay Office, 17 Caroline Street, 1864 & 1865 (Gubbins/47)

Wood, Henry
Jeweller, 13 Low Ousegate (Dir 1858)

Wray, Mark
Goldsmith, Free 1564 (SS102/5)
Swore an oath of good workmanship and paid 2s to the London company during their searches in the north. Also paid 3s for the swearing of an oath by his servant John Mennell, 17 July 1573 (LGC minute book L/158–9)

Wyke, William del
Goldsmith, Free 1385 (SS96/83)

Wylberfoss, Thomas de
Goldsmith, Free 1364 (SS96/59)

Wyman, Henry
[Goldsmith] and merchant, Free 1387 (SS96/85)
A naturalised German merchant (YAJ43/132n)
Married Agnes, daughter and coheiress of John Barden, litster (RHS)
Bailiff 1387/8 (Drake/361)
Corpus Christi play performed at the door of his house in Coney Street, 1399 (SS57/239)

Lord Mayor 1407, 1408 & 1409 (Drake/362)
Member of the Corpus Christi Guild (SS57/239)
Died 5 August 1411 buried at St Crux under a large blue marble, MI (RHS)
His wife died 22 September 1413 (RHS) During her widowhood she gave the Scrope Mazer to York Minster (SS57/240n)

Wyvell, John
Goldsmith, son of Richard Wyvell, girdler, Free by patrimony 1421 (SS96/131)

Yodson, Francis (Yowdson)
Goldsmith, Free 1562 (SS102/4)
Father of Thomas Yodson, carpenter, Free by patrimony 1594 (SS102/38)

Yppeswyche, John de
Goldbeater, Free 1394 (SS96/94)

Zachariah, Henry Isaac
Watchmaker, shop in Eastgate, Pickering, 1840–51 (Loomes/196)
Jeweller and watchmaker of Nunthorpe Crescent, died 2 December 1886 aged 76 buried York Cemetery grave 6492 old age (YCReg)
Wife, Elizabeth, died 1 January 1871 aged 65 buried York Cemetery grave 2885 asthma (YCReg)

Zachariah, John Allison
Son of Henry Isaac Zachariah, of Pickering, watchmaker, apprenticed to John Armstrong (q.v.), watchmaker, indenture 1 January 1848, 7 years (YCA D16/469)

APPENDIX 1 – References cited in the directory

Attreed	L.A. Attreed (ed.) *York House Books 1461–1490* (1991)
Aveling	J.C.H. Aveling *Catholic Recusancy in the City of York 1558–1791* (1970)
Bartlett	N. Bartlett *Lay Poll Tax Returns for the City of York 1381* (1953)
BIHR	Borthwick Institute of Historic Research
BL	British Library
BLI12	D.M. Smith 'A guide to the Archives of the Company of the Merchant Taylors in the City of York' *Borthwick List and Index* 12 (1994)
BTC16	D.M. Smith 'A guide to the Archives of the Merchant Adventurers of York' *Borthwick Texts and Calendars* 16 (1990)
Cartulary	Volume in the Archives of the Company of Merchant Adventurers of York
Cartwright	J.J. Cartwright *Chapters in the History of Yorkshire* (1872)
Cherry	J. Cherry *Goldsmiths* (1992)
Cooper	T.P. Cooper *The History of the Castle of York* (1911)
Cripps	W.J. Cripps *Old English Plate* (1926)
CCR	*Cal. Close Rolls 1360–1364*
CMI	*Cal. Misc. Inquisitions 1377–88*
CRP	*Cal. Rot. Pat.*
Culme	J. Culme *Directory of Gold and Silversmiths, Jewellers and Allied Traders 1838–1914* (1987)
Davies	R. Davies *Walks through the City of York* (1880)
Dinsdale	N.V. Dinsdale *The Old Clockmakers of Yorkshire* (1946)
Dir	Street or Trade Directory
Drake	F. Drake *Eboracum* (1736)
Ellis	Sir H. Ellis *Chronica Johannes de Oxenedes* (1859) pp. 315–325: Ms Hargrave Brit. Mus. Cod. membrane 313 f. 95b.
EYC	W. Farrer (ed.) *Early Yorkshire Charters*
Foster	J. Foster *Pedigrees of Yorkshire Families, West Riding* 2 Vols (1874) *North and East Ridings* (1874)
Gent	T. Gent *The Antient and Modern History of the Famous City of York* (1730)
Gent2	T. Gent *The Life of T. Gent, Printer of York written by himself* (1832)
Gill	M.A.V. Gill *A Directory of Newcastle Goldsmiths* (1980)
Gubbins	M. Gubbins *York Assay Office and Silversmiths 1776–1858* (1983)
H16	C.B. Norcliffe (ed.) 'The Visitation of Yorkshire in the years 1563 and 1564' *Harleian Society* 16 (1881)
Hearth	J. Hebden (ed.) *The Hearth Tax List for York City Parishes and Ainsty Wapentake, Lady Day 1672* (1992)
HM	Murray's York Pedigrees, Ms at York City Archives, York Minster Library, and York Reference Library
Jackson	C.J. Jackson *English Goldsmiths and their Marks* (1905, revised 1921)
Jewitt	L. Jewitt and W.H. StJ. Hope *The Corporation Plate and*

	Insignia of Office of the Cities and Corporate Towns of England and Wales 2 (1895)
Knipe	W. Knipe *Criminal Chronology of York Castle* (1867)
Law	Law R.J. 'Henry Hindley of York 1701–1771' *Antiquarian Horology* (June 1971 and September 1972)
Lee	W. Lee *York Silver 1475–1858* (1972, reprinted 1981)
LG	London Gazette
LGC	London Goldsmiths' Company
Loomes	B. Loomes *Yorkshire Clockmakers* (1985)
LRW	L.R. Wheatley, unpublished 'Register of the Members of the York Mercers' Guild 1420–1502'.
Malden	J. Malden *Register of York Freemen 1680–1986* (1989)
Merch Adv Co	Company of Merchant Adventurers *List of Members and Governors* (1966)
Palliser	D.M. Palliser *Tudor York* (1979)
Park	G.R. Park *The Parliamentary Representation of Yorkshire* (1886)
Pedersen	F Pedersen *'Romeo and Juliet in Stonegate': a medieval marriage in crisis* (1995) Borthwick Paper No 87
Poll	*The State of the Poll for Members of Parliament to represent the City of York* (1741, 1758, 1784, 1807, 1818, 1820, 1830)
PReg	Parish Register
PRO	Public Record Office 'Apprenticeship Books' IR1– per M. Gubbins
Pullein	C. Pullein *The Pulleyns of Yorkshire* (1915)
Radley	J. Radley 'York Waterworks and other waterworks in the north before 1800' *Transactions of the Newcomen Society* 39 (1966–7)
Raine	A. Raine *Mediaeval York* (1955)
Reddaway	T.F. Reddaway *The Early History of the Goldsmiths' Company 1327–1509* (1975)
Rel	The Monumental Brass and Will of Christopher Harrington, Goldsmith of York, 1614 *The Reliquary* NS vi (1892) pp 211–5
RHS	R.H. Skaife *York Civic Officials* Ms at York City Library
Setchell	J.R.M. Setchell 'Henry Hindley & Son, Clock and Instrument Makers and Engineers of York' *Yorkshire Philosophical Society Report* (1972)
StMSp	St Michael, Spurriergate, Church Warden's Accounts, Borthwick Institute PR Y/MS4.
SRJ	Rees Jones, S. *Medieval Title Deeds for the City of York 1080–1530* (computer work plus documentation) Colchester: ESRC Data Archive (1996).
SS30	J. Raine (ed.) 'Testmenta Eboracensia – a selection of Wills from the Registry at York 2' *Surtees Society* 30 (1855)
SS35	J. Raine (ed.) 'The Fabric Rolls of York Minster' *Surtees Society* 35 (1859)
SS41	W.D.H. Longstaffe (ed.) 'Heraldic Visitation of the Northern Counties in 1530 by Thomas Tonge' *Surtees Society* 41 (1863)
SS53	J. Raine (ed.) 'Testamenta Eboracensia – a selection of Wills from the Registry at York 4' *Surtees Society* 53 (1869)

SS57	R.H. Skaife 'The Register of the Guild of the Corpus Christi in the City of York' *Surtees Society* 57 (1872)
SS96	Collins, F. 'Register of the Freemen of the City of York, Vol 1, 1272–1558' *Surtees Society* 96 (1897)
SS102	Collins, F. 'Register of the Freemen of the City of York, Vol 2, 1559–1759' *Surtees Society* 102 (1900)
SS106	J.W. Clay (ed.) 'Testmenta Eboracensia – a selection of Wills from the Registry at York 6' *Surtees Society* 106 (1902)
SS120	M. Sellars 'York Memorandum Book A/Y Part 1 1376–1419' *Surtees Society* 120 (1912)
SS129	M Sellars (ed.) 'The York Mercers and Merchant Adventurers 1356–1917' *Surtees Society* 129 (1918)
SS186	J.W. Percy 'York Memorandum Book B/Y' *Surtees Society* 186 (1973)
SS192	R.B. Dobson (ed.) 'York City Chamberlains' Account Rolls 1396–1500' *Surtees Society* 192 (1980)
Taylor	E.W. Taylor and J.S. Wilson *At the Sign of the Orrery* (n.d. but 1950 revised 1960)
Thoresby2	'Miscellanea' *Publications of Thoresby Society* 2 (1891)
Walker	J.E.S. Walker *Hull and East Riding Clocks* (1982)
White	W. White, Manuscript Plans of the Streets of York as they appeared in January 1782, York Reference Library
Wilson	*Eboracum* (1788) Vol 2, printed for T. Wilson and R. Spence
YAJ4	E. Peacock (ed.) 'York Subsidy Roll' *Yorkshire Archaeological Journal* 4 (1877)
YAJ6	J. Raine 'Marske in Swaledale' *Yorkshire Archaeological Journal* 6 (1881)
YAJ17	'Yorkshire Deeds' *Yorkshire Archaeological Journal* 17 (1903)
YAJ18	M. Stephenson 'Monumental Brasses in the City of York' *Yorkshire Archaeological Journal* 18 (1905)
YAJ29	H.G. Baker 'The York Goldsmiths, an unrecorded maker's mark' *Yorkshire Archaeological Journal* 29 (1929)
YAJ35	J.S. Purvis 'Notes from the Diocesan Registry at York' *Yorkshire Archaeological Journal* 35 (1943)
YAJ43	J.I. Leggett 'The 1377 Poll Tax Return for the City of York' *Yorkshire Archaeological Journal* 43 (1971)
YAJ49	M.A.V. Gill 'The Latter Days of the York Assay Office' *Yorkshire Archaeological Journal* 49 (1977)
YAJ50	D.M. Palliser 'York's Earliest Administrative Record: The Husgabel Roll of *c.*1284' *Yorkshire Archaeological Journal* 50 (1978)
YAJ57	D.M. Palliser 'A Regional Capital as Magnet: Immigrants to York, 1477–1566'; A. Bennett 'The Mangies of Hull, a Family of Provincial Goldsmiths' *Yorkshire Archaeological Journal* 57 (1985)
YAJ60	A. Bennett 'The Goldsmiths of Church Lane, Hull: 1527–1784' *Yorkshire Archaeological Journal* 60 (1988)
YASES3	T.M. Fallow and H.B. McCall 'Yorkshire Church Plate 1: The City of York, the North Riding, the East Riding' *Yorkshire Archaeological Society Extra Series* 3 (1912)
YASRS6	F. Collins (ed.) 'Wills in the York Registry 1389–1514'

	Yorkshire Archaeological Society Record Series 6 (1889)
YASRS11	F. Collins (ed.) 'Wills in the York Registry 1514–1553' *Yorkshire Archaeological Society Record Series* 11 (1891)
YASRS14	F. Collins (ed.) 'Wills in the York Registry 1554–1568' *Yorkshire Archaeological Society Record Series* 14 (1893)
YASRS21	W. Brown (ed.) 'Yorkshire Lay Subsidy 1301' *Yorkshire Archaeological Society Record Series* 21 (1897)
YASRS24	F. Collins (ed.) 'Wills in the York Registry 1594–1602' *Yorkshire Archaeological Society Record Series* 24 (1898)
YASRS28	F. Collins (ed.) 'Wills in the York Registry 1612–1619' *Yorkshire Archaeological Society Record Series* 28 (1900)
YASRS35	F. Collins (ed.) 'Wills in the York Registry 1628–1636' *Yorkshire Archaeological Society Record Series* 35 (1905)
YASRS38	F. Collins (ed.) 'Wills etc. from the Dean and Chapters Court 1321–1636' *Yorkshire Archaeological Society Record Series* 38 (1907)
YASRS39	W. Brown (ed.) 'Yorkshire Deeds 1' *Yorkshire Archaeological Society Record Series* 39 (1909)
YASRS43	J.W. Clay (ed.) 'Pavers' Marriage Licences Part II' *Yorkshire Archaeological Society Record Series* 43 (1911)
YASRS46	J.W. Clay (ed.) 'Pavers' Marriage Licences Part III' *Yorkshire Archaeological Society Record Series* 46 (1912)
YASRS48	J.W. Clay (ed.) 'Yorkshire Monasteries, Suppression Papers' *Yorkshire Archaeological Society Record Series* 48 (1913)
YASRS49	E.W. Crossley (ed.) 'Wills in the York Registry 1660–1665' *Yorkshire Archaeological Society Record Series* 49 (1913)
YASRS50	W. Brown (ed) 'Yorkshire Deeds 2' *Yorkshire Archaeological Society Record Series* 50 (1914)
YASRS60	E.W. Crossley (ed.) 'Wills in the York Registry 1666–1672' *Yorkshire Archaeological Society Record Series* 60 (1920)
YASRS74	Miscellanea including 'Lay Subsidy Rolls for NR and the City of York, 1 Edward III [1327]' *Yorkshire Archaeological Society Record Series* 74 (1929)
YASRS137	H. Richardson (ed.) 'Court Rolls of the Manor of Acomb II' *Yorkshire Archaeological Society Record Series* 137 (1978)
YASRS148	Tringham, N.J. (ed.) 'Charters of the Vicars Choral of York Minster: City of York and its suburbs to 1546' *Yorkshire Archaeological Society Record Series* 148 (1993)
YAYAS34	D. Poole 'Victorian York – European Influence on Commerce' *YAYAS Times* 34 (November 1996)
YCA	York City Archives
YCh	*York Chronicle*
YCReg	York Cemetery Registers
YEP	*Yorkshire Evening Press*
YG	*Yorkshire Gazette*
YH	*York Herald*
YkCo	*York Courant*
YkHist13	P.M. Stell and A. Hawkyard 'The Lay Subsidy of 1334 for York' *York Historian* 13 (1996)
YML	York Minster Library
YWCWG	York Womens' and Craftsmen' Wills Group Database

Astley, William	WA	Clark, Richard	AC
Barber, Cattle and North	BC&N		RC
	BC&N	Etherington, William	WE
	J·B G·C W·N	Foster, William	FW
Barber, James	JB	Geldart, Joshua	IG
	JB	Gibson, George	GG
	JB	Gill, Mark	MG
Barber and North	JB WN		MG
	JB WN	Goldsborough, Charles	CO
	B&N	Gylmyn, Robert	RG
Barber and Whitwell	JB WW		RG
Beckwith, Robert	RB	Hampston and Prince	HP
Bell, John	I·B		HP
Best, John	BE		I·H I·P
Best, Marmaduke	MB		
Bryce, Francis	FB		H&P
Busfield, William	WB		I·H P
	WB		I·P·H
	·Bu·		I·H P
Camidge, John	IC		
Casson, Sem	SC	Hampston, Prince & Cattles	HPC
Casson, Robert	RC		HP&C
Cattell, William	WC		H·P & Cs
Cattle, Robert	R·C		H·P & C
Cattle and Barber	RC JB	Harrington, Christopher	CH
Chewe, Richard	RC		

148

Harrington, Robert

Harrington, Thomas

Hunton, Christopher

Hutchinson, William

Jackson, Edward

Kirby, Rowland

Kitchin, George

Langwith, John

Lee, Henry

Luty, George

Mady, John

Mangy, Christopher

Mangy, George

Mangy, Thomas

Marsh, Philemon

Mascall, William

Oliver, John

Pearson, Peter

Plumer, James

Plumer, John

Rawnson, William

Reed, Clement

Rhoades, Charles

Smith, John

Symson, Thomas

Tempest, Francis

Thompson, John

Turner, Daniel

Waddy, Thomas

Waite, Thomas

Waite, William

Watson, Christopher

Watson and Bell

Whitehill, Christopher

Williamson, Robert, I

Williamson, Robert, II

Williamson, William

Unidentified Maker's Marks

(M)	1564		1572		1709
	1564	(heart)	1568 & 1570		1780
		(D)	1623	[ES]	1790
[W]	1568		1626	**AB**	1843

Maker's Marks of York Goldsmiths registered at other Assay Offices

Buckle, Joseph	BV	Newcastle
Grant, William	Bv	Newcastle
Buckle, Stephen	SB	Newcastle
Cameo Engraving Co (see Walter Myers)	WM	Sheffield
Cattle, Barbara	BC	Sheffield and Birmingham
Chapman, George	GC	Birmingham
Grant, William	WG	Birmingham
Greenwood, William Francis	WFG	Sheffield & London
Hopper, A.E. & Son	AEH & S	Sheffield
Reggilla Jewels (see Cussins, Regge)	JC & RC	Sheffield
Veal, Bernard U.	BUV	Sheffield

APPENDIX 3 – York Town Marks and Date Letters

1. Town Marks

a.   *b.*   *c.*   *d.*

a.   Half fleur–de–lys and half leopard's head used before 1697.

b. c. & d.

Varieties of mark, based on the coat of arms of York, used after 1700

2. Date Letters

Year	Letter	Year	Letter	Year	Letter	Year	Letter	Year	Letter
1559-60	A*	1583-84	a	1607-08	a	1631-32	a	1655-56	A
1560-61	B	1584-85	b	1608-09	B	1632-33	b	1656-57	B
1561-62	C	1585-86	c*	1609-10	C	1633-34	c	1657-58	C
1562-63	D	1586-87	d*	1610-11	D	1634-35	d	1658-59	D
1563-64	E*	1587-88	e	1611-12	E	1635-36	e	1659-60	E
1564-65	F	1588-89	f*	1612-13	F	1636-37	f	1660-61	F
1565-66	G*	1589-90	g*	1613-14	G	1637-38	g	1661-62	G
1566-67	H	1590-91	h	1614-15	H	1638-39	h	1662-63	H
1567-68	I*	1591-92	i*	1615-16	I	1639-40	i	1663-64	J
1568-69	K	1592-93	k	1616-17	k	1640-41	k	1664-65	K
1569-70	L	1593-94	l	1617-18	L*	1641-42	l	1665-66	L
1570-71	M	1594-95	m	1618-19	M	1642-43	m	1666-67	M
1571-72	N*	1595-96	n	1619-20	N	1643-44	n*	1667-68	N
1572-73	O	1596-97	o*	1620-21	O	1644-45	o	1669-69	O
1573-74	P	1597-98	p	1621-22	P	1645-46	p*	1669-70	P
1574-75	Q	1598-99	q*	1622-23	Q	1646-47	q*	1670-71	Q
1575-76	R	1599-1600	r	1623-24	R	1647-48	r*	1671-72	R
1576-77	S	1600-01	s*	1624-25	S	1648-49	s	1672-73	S
1577-78	T	1601-02	t	1625-26	T	1649-50	t	1673-74	T
1578-79	V*	1602-03	u*	1626-27	U	1650-51	u	1674-75	U
1579-80	W*	1603-04	w*	1627-28	W	1651-52	w*	1675-76	W
1580-81	X*	1604-05	x	1628-29	X*	1652-53	x	1676-77	X
1581-82	Y	1604-05	y*	1629-30	Y	1653-54	y	1677-78	Y
1582-83	Z	1606-07	z*	1630-31	Z	1654-55	z	1678-79	Z

*Date letters conjectured from adjacent observations

Year	Letter	Year	Letter	Year	Letter	Year	Letter	Year	Letter
1679-80	A	1701-02	A	1787-88	A	1812-13	a	1836-37	A
1680-81	B	1702-03	B	1788-89	B	1813-14	a	1837-38	B
1681-82	C	1703-04	C	1789-90	C	1814-15	a	1838-39	C
1682-83	D	1704-05	D	1790-91	d	1815-16	d	1839-40	D
1683-84	E	1705-06	E*	1791-92	e	1816-17	d	184--41	E
1684-85	F	1706-07	F	1792-93	e	1817-18	f	1841-42	F
1685-86	G	1707-08	G	1793-94	g	1818-19	g	1842-43	G
1686-87	H	1708-09		1794-95	h	1819-20	h	1843-44	H
1687-88	I	1709-10	H	1795-96	i	1820-21	i	1844-45	I
1688-89	K	1710-11	k*	1796-97	K	1821-22	k	1845-46	K
1689-90	L	1711-12	l*	1797-98	L	1822-23	l	1846-47	L
1690-91	M	1712-13	m	1798-99	M	1823-24	m	1847-48	M
1691-92	N	1713-14	n*	1799-1800	N	1824-25	n	1848-49	N
1692-93	O	1714-15	o	1800-01	O	1825-26	o	1849-50	O
1693-94	P	1715-16	p*	1801-02	P	1826-27	p	1850-51	P
1694-95	Q	1776-77	A*	1802-03	Q	1827-28	q	1851-52	Q
1695-96	R	1777-78	B*	1803-04	R	1828-29	r	1852-53	R
1696-97	S	1778-79	C*	1804-05	S	1829-30	s	1853-54	S
		1779-80	D	1805-06	T	1830-31	t	1854-55	T
		1780-81	E	1806-07	U	1831-32	u	1855-56	U
		1781-82	F	1807-08	V	1832-33	u	1856-57	V
		1782-83	G	1808-09	W	1833-34	w	1857-58	W
		1783-84	H	1809-10	X	1834-35	x	1858-59	X
		1784-85	J	1810-11	Y	1835-36	z		
		1785-86	J	1811-12	Z				
		1786-87	J						

The date when a date letter was changed is not known but it does not appear, as might be logically expected, to have been New Year's Day. In 1586 (see page 8) by order of the lord mayor and his court the new searchers for the following year were elected on 29 July and this date may also mark the start of the next date letter. The only positive evidence is a statement by the Inspector General of Stamps and Taxes who indicated that the change took place on 13 August in 1851 (Gubbins/33). The tables thus show a range of two years for each date letter.

After 1776 the date letters are based on the work of Martin Gubbins who has spent many years observing and noting silver marks. His conclusions have been published in his book on the *York Assay Office and Silversmiths 1776–1858* (1983) pp 70–73 and *Jackson's Silver and Gold Marks of England, Scotland and Ireland* (1989) edited by Ian Pickford, pp 464–7. That on five occasions a date letter would appear to have been repeated in one or more subsequent years is a further indication that the organisation of the York Assay Office was not too carefully supervised by the Wardens of the York Goldsmiths' Company

APPENDIX 4 – The Ordinances of the Goldsmiths

1. 5 March 1410/11   York Memorandum Book A/Y Vol I SS120/74–77

Orfeverers – Goldsmythes [original in French]

[fo. 29] Be it remembered that whereas the debate and dispute lately moved amongst the craftsmen goldsmiths of York in order to elect their searchers whereby some goldsmiths of the said craft wish to have three searchers and others two and on this matter the said craftsmen of the goldsmiths come before the mayor and seek his aid and governance, and furthermore they agree to abide by his decision and judgement and his brother alderman and other wise men of the council of the chamber; and on this matter the honourable lord mayor on proper consideration by the most worthy men of the city Henry Wyman, John de Bolton, Nicholays Blakburn, Thomas Santon, Robert Howm, William del Alne, Wauter Askam and Thomas del More and Robert de Lokton, sheriffs, Johan de Moreton, recorder, William Lambard, Johan Hewyk, Robert Gaunt, William Berkeued, William Ormesheued, Johan Lofthous, Galfridus Sauvage, chamberlains, Henrye Rothwell, Amond Askham, William de Bothe and many others, the fifth day of March in this year of our lord king Henry the fourth [1410–11] it was agreed by the said honourable lord mayor, aldermen, sheriffs and all the said good people, that from henceforth there shall be two searchers of the said craft, English men born, and no more; and now in this matter, after the aforesaid agreement and judgement made in the aforesaid form, two goldsmiths, that is to say Johan Cleveland and William Skyres, were elected searchers and sworn to occupy the said office; and beyond this it was resolved by the said honourable lord and good people aforesaid that, whereas the goldsmiths bring their touchstones and mark so that their goods can be stamped with the die as the statute requires, and if they do not have a touchstone nor a die they are to make a new touchstone and die complying with the rule as the common law demands.

And if any master of the said craft sells or offers for sale any gold or silver article which appertains to their said craft before it is stamped with the common assay stamp of the said city and its die, he who sells the said article shall forfeit 6s 8d, half to the use of the commonalty of the same city and the other half to the profit of the said makers of girdles, daggers, collars of nobility and other things that cannot ever carry the said assay stamp only excepting those goods which cannot carry the said assay stamp shall be marked with the die of the owner, of the aforesaid pain of paying in form abovesaid each time any one of them does anything contrary to that ordinance, so that all things of gold [illegible] or of silver made in the said city shall be known to be good and lawful [illegible] other things made in other parts of the kingdom of England, etc.

[fo. 29b] Item it is ordained that each man of the said craft who takes any apprentice shall send for two men of the same craft to hear their agreements, that no fraud nor deceit shall be done between the master and his apprentice; on pain of 6s 8d, paid in the manner stated above.

Item it is ordained that no master of the said craft takes any apprentice for a lesser term than the term of seven years, on pain of 6s 8d, paid as is stated above, each time any master of the said craft does the contrary and is found guilty.

Item it is ordained that if any apprentice leaves his master in anyway before the end of the term agreed with him, that no master hires him afterwards for a lesser term than the terms not completed with his first master on pain of 6s 8d as stated above.

Item it is ordained that, if any stranger of the same craft comes to the said city to work in the same craft, no master shall hire him for lesser term than one year, and also his work shall be searched by the searchers of the said craft, and according to their good discretion and advice, set the wage he shall get; and if any master of the said craft hires the said stranger for a larger sum or a smaller than that which the said searchers have set for him, he shall pay 6s 8d in the manner as stated above.

2. 10 April 1561   House Book B33

(fo 11b) The auncient ordynauncs of the mystery or occupation of goldsmythes of the Citie of York diligently perused and examyned by the right worshipfull Parsyvall Craforth, Mayour, the Aldermen and Pryvay Counsell of the sayd Citie of Yorke assembled in the Consell Chambre apon Ousebrig, and by the said Mayour, Aldermen and Consell with the full consenlt of Thomas Symson and Robert Gylmyn, serchars, and other the goodmen maisters of the sayd craft beyng alsoo present were than and there dewly reformed etc. to be from thensforth fermely observed and kept for ever to the worship of the said Citie, common profit of the people and honesty of the sayd occupacon.

(fo. 12) Inprimis the vth day of Marche in the xijth yere of the reigne of Kyng Henry the iiijth [1410/11] it was ordeyned by the Lord Mayor, Aldermen, Shirefs and other the most honest and substanttiall persones of the said Citie of York with the full aggreement of the said wholle occupacon of goldsmiths that frome thensforth there sholde be twooe serchars of the said occupacon, Englishe men borne, and no moe. And over that it was then ordeyned that the said goldsmythes sholde bryng their towche, so that thar work might be approved and to towched with the pounce of this Citie called the half lepard head and half floure de luce accordyng as the statut purportith. And if they have not a towche or pounce that then they shold cause one newe towche and pounce to be made in accomplishement of justice as the common lawe it demandith; and that every goldsmyth shall make his proper towche or marke to be knowne to the serchars for the tyme beyng apon payne to forfayte iijs iiijd; and that no goldsmyth shall work any worse golde than the towche of Paryse apon payne of forfayture, onles it be in ryngs or other small jewells that maybe suffered to be wrought of the same that is brought to theym. And that no goldsmyth shall worke worse a lay then sterlyng and that it be not delyvered unto it be searched by the serchars and the said towche of the Citie and his mark sett to; and that no serchar sett the Citie towche to worse than sterlyng apon payne of forfayture the duble valewe, except that there nede sowder in the makyng, whiche shalbe allowed accordyng as the sowder is necessarie to be wrought in the same.

And yf any maister of the said Craft sell or putt to sale any thing of gold or sylver whiche belongeth to their said Craft before it be towched with the Common towche of the said Citie, and also the mark of hym that ther said thing will sell, that he sholde forfayte vjs viijd; thone half to the use of the Comonaltie of the same Citie and thother half to the profett of the said Craft. Except harnesys of girdles, daggers, collers of gentiles and other things under the weight of an unce that may not suffre to beare the said towche, whiche shalbe towched onely with the mark of hym that maketh it upon payne abovesaid and to be payed in forme aforesaid at every tyme that any of theym doeth contrary to this ordynance. So that everything made within this Citie may be knowne for good and lawfull frome other things made in other places within this realme of England.

Item it is further ordeyned that yf any man of the said craft werke any evill gold or sylver, that thing that is so made shalbe broken and putt ageyne into the fyre to purifie and to fyne and to be made ageyne perfectly, and he that trespaced shall forfayte and lose xxs to the Chamber and craft by even porcons; and at the secund tyme xls and the thirde tyme cs; and if he will not so be chastised he shall forsware the craft or be putt forth of the Citie.

Item that accordyng to the statute none of the said artificers or any other shall gilde nor sylver any ryngs, beads, harneys for girdles or suche other made of coper or laten; except ornaments of holy cherche; so that in the foote or some other part of every suche ornament (fo. 12b) the latton or copper appere playnly; and except after spurres for knights and apparell that belongith to a Barone and above that estate apon payne to forfayt vli in forme aforesaid.

Item that no goldsmyth sett any counterfeyt stone in gold except it be a naturall stone apon payne conteyned in the statut therof.

Item that the serchars of the said occupacon shall trewly make searche as oft as they shall think necessarie and dewly present fawts to the Lord Mayour accordyng to there oathe.

Item that no man denye the searchers at any tyme to make searche nor revyle theym at any tyme neither at his shoppe nor at any other place, whills they be searchers in payne of forfayture of vjs viijd

Item yf there be cause why that the occupacon sholde mete for the wele of the said Citie and be warned by the searchers to mete at a place convenient at a certayne howre, he that is awaye without reasonable cause to pay xijd.

Item that no goldsmyth shall sett no jornay man on worke but for xiiij dayes and yf he doe without the leave of the searchers he shall pay iijs iiijd in forme aforesaid.

Item that the pageant maisters make a dewe accompte of the money and of the playing geare unto thoccupacon on Saynt Dunstaynes even or ells the morowe after apon payne of xijd a pece.

Item that the crownes nor gownes be not lent to none under viijd a pece, and that it be payd or they be delyvered, except it be to some of thoccupacon and the serchars to make accompte therof.

Item that no maister of the said craft shall take any aprentice for lesse terme than seven yeares apon payne of tenne marks – and at the comyng in of the said apprentice within a month to paye viijd to the craft and his name to be entred in our booke, and at thende of his terme to be free, paying his lawfull dewties to the said occupacon; and if it chanse the maister of suche apprentice to die duryng the said apprenticeship than suche shall serve still with his maistres yf she have a jornay man sufficiently conyng to learne hym or ells the same apprentice to be sett over to some other maister of the said occupacon by discreccon of the searchers.

Item that none that hath served his apprentiship within the said Citie shall occupie as maister in the said craft before that he be approved by the serchars of the same that he be hable and conyng workman in the said craft apon payne of forfayture of xiiijs.

(fo. 13) Item that no stranger ne other that hath not bene apprentice within this Citie by the space of seven yeres or moare shall not sett up nor occupie as maister of the said occupacon of goldsmythes within this Citie apon payne of forfayture of xli; except suche stranger or others that hath not bene apprentise as is aforesaid, be first allowed by my Lord Mayour and serchers of the said occupacon for tyme beyng, and doe alsoe paye before he occupie as maister of the same occupacon xli thone half to the said Chamber and th'other half to the said occupation.

3. 14 November 1584 House book B28/164b

Instructions for MPs (unsuccessful)

Item that the searchers of occupacons within this Cittie may have search of suche artificers as do dwell within the close of York.

4. 3 February 1585 House book B28/185 & 185b

Memorandum that the seaven and twentie day of Januray in the seaven and twentie yeare of the Reyne of our Soveraigne Lady elizabeth by the Grace of god Quene of England ffrance and Ireland defender of the faithe and in the time of the maioraltie of Thomas Appleyard lord maior of the Cittie of Yorke at the request of the maysters and brethren of goldsmythes of the cittie of Yorke all the aforesaid antient ordinance were by the said lord maior and his worshipfull brethren aldermen and privie counsell of the said Cittie diliberatlie perused and thereupon by consent of the said goldsmiths further augmented amended and established as followeth viz.

First wheras complayntes and variances now moved amongst the occupacon of goldesmiths of this Cittie as well concerninge the chosinge of their searchers as also concerninge the auditinge and presentinge of ther accomptes and the most parte of the said occupacon did nowe personally appeare in this court, And for that that [sic] by ther ordinall it did not appeare howe or in what order the premisses shold be donne and executed, it is this day for the better quietnes of the said occupacon, and the benefit of this Cittie, aggreed and ordaned as followeth

First as towchinge the eleccon of seachers of the said occupacon it is ardayned that from henceforth the old searchers of the said occupacon shall yearlie on th fowerth day next after the feast day of Sainte James thappostle so that the same be not Sondays and if the same fowerthe day happen to be on Sondays then the morowe next after, in peaceable manner call togethere the bretheren of the said occupacon in Saint Anthoines Hall and then and ther the said old searchers shall takes the voyces of all the bretheren of the said occupacon then and there assembled for the eleccon of two new searchers fro the yeare following. (fo 185b) Which newe searchers are to be elected and chosen by the most voyces of the said occupacon then so assembled provided alwayes that the old searchers for the tyme beinge shall have no voyces at the said eleccon and the said two newe searchers to be elected and chosen generallye out of the whole occupacon and if it happen that the olde searchers or eyther of them shall chance to be chosen newe searchers or eyther of them so by most voyces chosen to remayne Searcher or Searchers for the next year followinge.

Item as towchinge the auditing of the accomptes of the searchers it is ordayned that the searchers for the tyme beinge shall yearlie at the daye of the said eleccon before the maysters of the said occupacon departe from their eleccon, make theris accompte of all suche somes of money and other thinges as they shall receyve by vertue of their office and deliver the same over to the new searchers and the said old searchers to have allowance for their necessarye expenses and charges towching suche money as they shall have disbursed for the said occupacon and the same allowance to be allowed and presented by the most voyces of the said occupacon ther assembled Provided that if any materiall contraversye happen to be

157

emongst the said occupacon towching the premisses that the lord maior fro that tyme being to order and determyne the same.

Item it is ordaned and agreed that the searchers of the said occupacon now being chosen shall be sworne and they to continewe in their office till the fowerth daie next after Saint James daie next.

5. 4 November 1596 House Book B31/228

And whereas John Sharr goldsmyth was heretofore comyt to ward for buying moulten silver of a person unknowne which is suspected not to be trewlie or well come to by the seller Nowe the said John Sharre being called before thes presentes is enjoyned to loke for the partie and to cause him to be brought befor my L maior befoer St Andrewes daie next and in regard that he must be at libertie so to do he is asyet respited his further ponishment.

Also the goldsmyths are enjoyned to bring in ther ordinary the next court daie to be perused whether ther be any article to prohibit buying of moulten silver of persones unknowne and suchlike suspected jewells or silver to thend that no such order be therein an order to that effecte mat be added thereunto.

6. 23 July 1606 House Book B33/23b & 24

And nowe it is agreed that thes articles followinge shalbe incerted into the Goldsmithes ordinarie to be observed and kepte as parcell of ther ordinarie
First in regard that the companye of goldsmythes within the said Cittye are growne to be a great companye and so likely to encrease It is ordred and agreed, that no person or persons professinge or using the occupacon of a goldsmythe and not haveinge served as an apprentice within the said cittye and with some free brother of the same companye shalbe from hensfurthe admitted a freman of this Cittye without the consent of the Lord Maior of the said cittye and the Aldermen his Brethern first obteyned, and the searchers of the said occupacon not beinge hable to objecte against the sufficyenccye of the said parties.

And it is farther ordred and agreed, that no free cittizen or other Inhabitant within the said city or suburbes thereof shall sett any goldsmythe dwellinge in the saide cittye or suburbs thereof or within anye Libertye or previledged place in or nere adioyninge to the said cittye on work (the same goldsmythe not beinge a freman of this cittye and of the same companye) in makenge alteringe or exchainginge of any manner of plate or anye other thinge belonginge to the said occupacon of a goldsmythe upon paine of forfeyture of xls. to the use of the Maior and comonaltie of the said cittye (excepte suche work as the said goldsmythes cannot so well performe) without the consent of the Lord Maior for the time beinge first obteyned.

Also it is agreed and ordred, that no goldsmythe dwellinge in the Mynstergarthe or within the said cittye or suburbs thereof (not beinge free of the same companye of goldsmythes) shall have the benifytt to have ther plate or other thinges by them made to be pounced with the towche and marke belonginge to this cittye called the half Leopard head and half flower de Luce without the consent and appointment of the Lord Maior for the time beinge.

Also it is agreed and ordred, that no free brother of the same companye of goldsmyths shall from hensfurthe work anye manner of work belonginge to the occupacon of a goldsmythe with any goldsmythe (not beinge a freeman and a free brother of the same companye) within the said cittye or precinctes thereof upon paine of xls. to be forfeyted to thuse aforesaid for everye time so doinge.

9. 18 August 1695 House Book B39/26b

Itt is ordered that the Ordinary belonging to the gold smiths be kept by the Lord Mayor till further order.

10. The York Goldsmiths' Company – W. Hargrove (1818) pp. 658–60

Not having yet been noticed, deserves a little attention here; particularly as the Assay Office connected with it, is the only relic of the Mint which we have already described as having been once established in York.

In the 12th of William III, an act was passed for amending former acts to appoint Wardens and Assay Masters, for assaying wrought plate, in the cities of London, York, Exeter, Bristol, Chester, and Norwich; the only places in England, where gold and silver could then be assayed and stamped. In the first year of queen Ann, however, Newcastle–upon–Tyne was incorporated with the same powers. Birmingham and Sheffield have also Assay Offices, but they are for silver only.

By the preceding legislative enactment, it was commanded that the Goldsmiths and Silversmiths, who having served a regular apprenticeship, were free of, and inhabiting, any of those cities, should be incorporated into a company, and be called the company of Goldsmiths, or wardens and assayers of each such said city. Thus formed, they were authorized to elect two wardens yearly, and to appoint an assay–master, or assayer, for each company; which assay–master is obliged to take an oath before the chief magistrate of the city, that he will act in conformity with the several legislative enactments. This officer is under the direction of the wardens, and has an office appointed, where the manufacturers of gold and silver articles, must send their goods for his inspection and trial, relative to their respective qualities. If any articles thus sent, are found to be deficient of the regular standard, it is lawful for the wardens or assay–master, to destroy such articles, but not until the deficiency has been fully ascertained by three separate assays. The old standard for gold, is 22 carrats fine, and the new, 18 carrats: Silver 11 oz. 2 dwt. fine, viz: to every 11 oz. 2 dwt. of pure virgin silver, there are 18 dwt. of alloy; which alloy renders it of the same quality as the coin of the realm.

Consonant with the said acts of parliament, a note is sent with every parcel of plate, containing a list of all the articles, their separate and total weight, the year, the day of the month, and the christian and surname of the manufacturer. This to be delivered at the assay office, by nine o'clock in the morning; and the assay–master is obliged to weigh the articles, and if according to the standard, after the manufacturer's initials are marked with a punch, and the articles entered in the company's books, the assay–master must stamp a Lion passant, King's head, Leopard's head, and the arms of the city; also a numerical letter, denoting the year in which the plate was manufactured; and the whole must be ready for delivery to the owner, by five the same evening.

The assay days are Tuesday and Friday, in every week; and a duty is paid of one shilling and sixpence per oz. for silver, and seventeen shillings per oz. for gold. The charge of the assay master, for his trouble, must not, however, exceed sixpence in every pound, troy weight; but it is lawful for him to detain eight grains from every such pound of silver; the weight being, taken whilst the plate is in an unfinished state, and consequently much heavier than when it is completed. No fancy article need be stamped; only gold rings, mourning rings, watch cases, cups, buttons, &c.

The present assay–master, resides and has his office in Feasegate. A clerk is also appointed to keep the accounts, who receives a certain per centage out of the duty. The members, with the wardens, assay–master, and clerk, meet quarterly, to regulate and balance the accounts, and to attend to the general business of the company; such as forming bye–laws for themselves, appointing an assay–master, clerk, &c.

This privilege which York, with the other places enjoys, is not only highly beneficial to the revenue of the country; but prevents a system of gross fraud, which would otherwise be practised upon the public, and injure both society in general, and the honest tradesman in particular.

1   Communion cup: maker Robert Harrington, 1622
Photo: Courtesy of Richard Sykes

2   Sweetmeat dish: maker James Plumer, 1636, in York Minster Undercroft

Photo: Courtesy of the William Lee Collection

3 Wine cup: maker Robert Williamson, 1655
Photo: Courtesy of the William Lee Collection

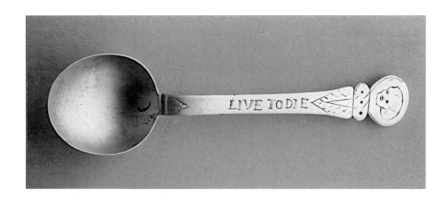

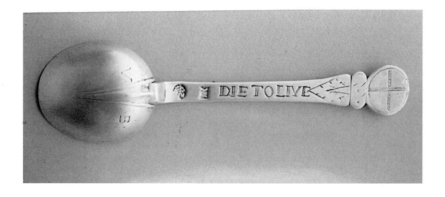

4　'Death's Head' spoon: maker Thomas Mangy, 1669, in York
Minster Undercroft

Photo: Courtesy of the William Lee Collection

5　Fork: maker Thomas Mangy, 1680

Photo: Courtesy of the William Lee Collection

6 Bleeding bowl: maker John Plumer, 1670
Photo: Courtesy of the William Lee Collection

7 Wax jack: maker William Busfield, 1695
Photo: Courtesy of the William Lee Collection

8   Peg tankard with 8 small pegs in a vertical row inside: maker John
Thompson, 1673
    Photo: Courtesy of Museum of Fine Arts, Boston, Massachusetts

9 Chinoiserie porringer: maker Thomas Mangy, 1676

Photo: Courtesy of Richard Sykes

10 Tankard: maker Marmaduke Best, 1677

Photo: Courtesy of Richard Sykes

11 Coffee pot: maker Hampston, Prince and Cattles, 1799
Photo: Courtesy of Richard Sykes

12 Thistle–shaped cup: maker James Barber and William Whitwell,
1821
Photo: Courtesy of the Company of Merchant Adventurers of York

13 Tankard with fox finial: maker Barber, Cattle and North, 1827
Photo: Courtesy of Richard Sykes

14 Johnnie Walker Ebor cup: maker Barbara Cattle, 1967